# Simulation of transport processes in soils

BALLARD

**Simulation  Monographs**

Simulation Monographs is a series on
computer simulation in agriculture and
its supporting sciences

# Simulation of transport processes in soils

C.T. de Wit and H. van Keulen

**Wageningen**
**Centre for Agricultural Publishing and Documentation**
**1972**

ISBN 90 220 0417 1

Cover design: Pudoc, Wageningen

Printed in Belgium

# Contents

This paper is the result of a project by students and research workers in Wageningen, interested in the simulation of transport processes in soils.

These are:

Agricultural University of Wageningen:
C. G. E. M. van Beek, G. H. Bolt, F. van Egmond, J. Goudriaan, P. J. J. Jakobs, H. van Keulen, H. Stricker, C. T. de Wit

IBS, Wageningen:
C. de Jonge, C. T. de Wit

ITAL, Wageningen:
M. J. Frissel

LIO, Wageningen:
M. Leistra

University of Iowa, Ames (Iowa, USA)
D. Barèl

# 1 Introduction

## 1.1 Purpose

The purpose of this book is to interest student and scientist in the simulation of transport processes in the soil: transport of heat, salts, ions and water in the unsaturated phase. These processes are characterized by a simultaneous change in the amount of energy or material with time and place. In mathematics, such distributive systems are described by partial differential equations, which are difficult to solve. Most problems that can be solved by analytical methods are so simple, that they are mainly of academical interest, but of little practical value. Training in analytical methods is very important, because this gives a good insight into the fundamental aspects of problems. However, the engineer or scientist faced with the task of finding reasonable quantitative solutions for practical problems can hardly use these methods and often much of his skill is lost in the mathematical handling of problems.

With problems where the elegant and not so elegant analytical solutions fail, solutions may be obtained by the brute force of the computer. Training in numerical mathematical methods and training in the use of the computer is then necessary. This training should be available at two levels.

For development purposes, advanced training in numerical methods and programming techniques is necessary, but apart from this, it is extremely useful to train students more inclined to engineering in such a way, that they are able to tackle their problems with a minimum expenditure of time and effort.

Therefore computing systems have been developed in recent years to handle problems of numerical integration. These systems are very much alike in their basic approach, but vary for different machines and in their level of sophistication. By far the most sophisticated languages are 'Continuous System Modeling Program (CSMP)', developed by IBM for its 360 series of machines, and other languages derived from it.

1

The student is introduced to this engineering approach. To read the book fruitfully, he should have an 'undergraduate' training in soil science and mathematics and a basic knowledge of FORTRAN.

Since CSMP is used throughout, it is advisable to have the 'User's manual of the system /360 Continuous System Modeling Program', available through IBM offices under the number H20-0367-2. Moreover, he should have the patience to invent some alternatives for the given solutions and possibly carry these out on a nearby computer that can handle the system.

Even persons who do not have access to CSMP or similar languages may gain enough insight in the problems to use a simulation system available to him or embark on programming in plain ALGOL or FORTRAN, although this is not advised.

## 1.2 Some principles of transport processes

The most important transport processes in soils are the transport of heat, water, solutes in the water (ions, organic substances) and gases ($CO_2$, $O_2$, water vapour). They can be described by some general equations.

It is assumed that the frictional forces during movement of a substance are proportional to the velocity of flow and compensate the driving force in full. As a consequence, a uniform motion results with a velocity in the same direction as and proportional to the driving force. The equation for the rate of flow of a substance is thus assumed to be:

$$FLOW = TRAN * DRIVING FORCE \qquad (1.1)$$

in which TRAN, the transport coefficient, is independent of the driving force.

The transport process must also satisfy the continuity condition, which is a direct consequence of the principle of the conservation of matter. Apart from the production or release of a substance or heat (i.e. the uptake of water or ions by roots, the heat of wetting and the release of $CO_2$ by micro-organisms) this continuity condition states simply that the rate of increase of a substance in a volume equals the net rate of flow over its boundaries.

For the diffusion of molecules the driving force is proportional to the concentration gradient and may be expressed in $g\,cm^{-3}\,cm^{-1}$. When

2

flow is expressed in $g\,cm^{-2}\,min^{-1}$ the transport coefficient has to be expressed in $cm^2\,min^{-1}$. The driving force for ions does not only depend on their concentration gradient, but also on the electromotive force which results from the presence of other ions. This will be considered later in detail.

Since conduction of heat is caused by the irregular thermal motion of molecules, heat flow may be treated in a similar way. The driving force is then proportional to the temperature gradient, which equals the gradient in volumetric heat content divided by the volumetric heat capacity of the soil. If the flow is expressed in $cal\,cm^{-2}\,min^{-1}$, the transport coefficient has the unit of $cal\,cm^{-1}\,min^{-1}\,°C^{-1}$.

The driving force for the flow of water in soil is the potential gradient, which may be expressed in $mbar\,cm^{-1}$. When the flow of water is in $g\,cm^{-2}\,min^{-1}$, the transport coefficient is in $g\,cm^{-2}\,min^{-1}\,mbar^{-1}$ (One mbar is about the pressure of a column of water of one cm). For horizontal flow and in the absence of other gradients, the potential gradient equals the gradient in volumetric moisture content, divided by the specific moisture content, which is the change in volumetric moisture content per unit change in potential. The gradient in moisture content has the unit $cm^3\,cm^{-3}\,cm^{-1}$, so that the unit of the transport coefficient is $cm^2\,min^{-1}$, when the flow is in $cm^3\,cm^{-2}\,min^{-1}$. With the transport of water, the transport coefficient depends on the friction between the water molecules and between the water molecules and the surface of the soil matrix and this friction increases rapidly with decreasing water content, that is with the increase of the contact surface between the matrix and the water per unit water. Hence, the transport coefficient for water depends largely on the moisture content of the soil, a dependence which should be carefully distinguished from the independence of the moisture gradient. The specific water content of the soil also depends on the moisture content, since large pores lose their water first.

Equation (1.1) has to be verified experimentally. It has been shown that it holds well enough for the movement of solutes, heat and water through the pores of a soil matrix. It should, however, be realised that movement of heat and solutes occurs also with the movement of water and that this movement has to be superimposed on the movement by diffusion of these substances.

3

# 2 Flow of heat

## 2.1 Basic approach

Fig. 1 shows a uniform soil column of finite length taken from an infinite slab and placed on an insulating layer. It is supposed that the temperature at the column's upper surface changes arbitrarily with time. To calculate the temperature as a function of depth and time, the column is divided into 25 equal compartments with thickness TCOM. Heat flow into and out of each compartment is calculated at any instant of time from the temperature difference between the compartments and the transport coefficient. Based on the continuity condition, these flows are realised over a short time interval to obtain the volumetric heat content of each compartment a finite instant of time later. The calculation is then repeated to advance another finite interval in time.

The calculation for any compartment, except the first and the last one, proceeds as follows.

The volumetric heat content and the temperature of the Nth compartment are given by VHTC(N) and TEMP(N), respectively (Fig. 1). At any instant of time, the temperature in each compartment may be calculated by dividing the volumetric heat content by the volumetric heat capacity (VHCAP) times TCOM.

The flow from compartment (N−1) to compartment (N) is represented by the symbol FLOW(N) and may be approximated according to Eqn (1.1) with

```
FLOW(N) = (TEMP(N-1) - TEMP(N)) *
COND/TCOM
```

COND is the heat conductivity, and TCOM the distance between the centres of the two compartments. This equation is only correct for infinite small compartments, but is applied here to compartments of finite size. The net flow into the Nth compartment is now

```
NFLOW(N) = FLOW(N) - FLOW(N+1)
```

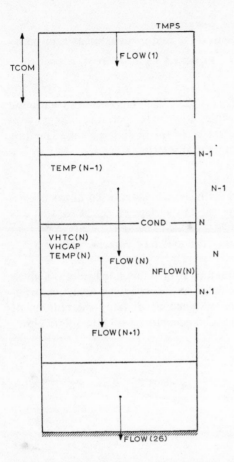

Fig. 1 | Geometry of the system and symbols, used in the program for the flow of heat in a homogeneous soil column.

As it is assumed that Eqn (1.1) holds for finite distances, it is also assumed that this net flow rate holds over a finite time interval DELT (delta time), so that the volumetric heat content of the Nth compartment a time DELT later is given by

$$VHTC(N)_{t+delt} = VHTC(N)_t + NFLOW(N) * DELT$$

The volumetric heat content at the beginning of the experiment must be given to start this numerical integration.

The flow rate from the surface into the first compartment is given by

```
FLOW(1) = (TMPS - TEMP(1)) * COND/
(0.5*TCOM)
```

in which the temperature of the surface (TMPS) is given by a forcing function, i.e. a function which states how the temperature changes with time, independent of the temperature of the underlying soil. The flow from the last compartment into the insulating layer is

```
FLOW(26) = 0.
```

The course of the temperature with depth, 4.8 and 9.6 hours after a stepwise change of temperature at the surface from 20 to 10°C, is given in Fig. 2, the volumetric heat capacity being $0.25$ cal cm$^{-3}$ °C$^{-1}$ and the thermal conductivity of the soil $0.06$ cal cm$^{-2}$ min$^{-1}$ °C$^{-1}$.

The points in the graph were obtained from a tabulated solution, given by Carslaw & Jaeger (1962), which is passed off as an analytical solution and the open circles were obtained by dividing the column of 50 cm into 25 layers of 2 cm each, advancing time with intervals of about

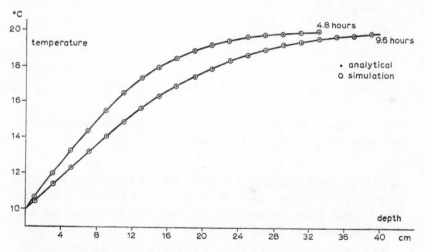

Fig. 2 | Temperature distribution in a profile, 4.8 and 9.6 hours after a sudden drop from 20° to 10°C at the surface.

10 minutes. The cyclic variation of the temperature at a depth of 3 and 9 cm generated by a cyclic variation at the surface with a period of 24 hours and an amplitude of 10 °C is given in Fig. 3. The crosses were obtained from an analytical solution, discussed by Van Wijk (1963) and the open circles were obtained by the above mentioned numerical method.

In both cases there is a good agreement between the numerical and analytical solution (in fact, both solutions differ only at the fourth digit) and this shows that the numerical method used here is fully acceptable. A numerical solution would not have any advantages, if it only gave answers that could be obtained analytically. However, it will be shown that it can also be used to calculate the course of temperature in the soil in a much more complicated situation: a problem where the conductivity and the volumetric heat capacity of the soil vary with depth and where the temperature at the surface is governed by the balance between incoming global radiation, outgoing

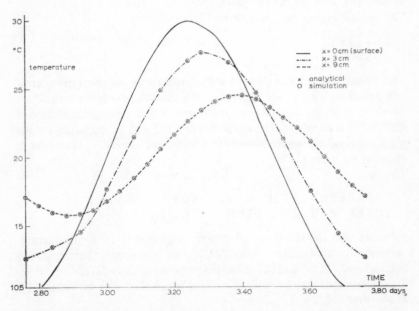

Fig. 3 | Temperature variation during one day, at 3 and 9 cm depth, generated by the given sinusoidal variation at the surface.

long wave radiation and exchange of heat with the air and the underlying soil.

Before this is done, it is at first necessary to show how the simple numerical calculation, discussed in this section, is actually carried out.

## 2.2 A CSMP program for the heat flow in a uniform soil

The problem of heat flow will be programmed in the Continuous System Modelling Program to show the suitability of this simulation language for solving distributive systems. The CSMP functions and constructions that are used will be explained in the text in a way that should be intelligible without a CSMP Manual, although it is an advantage to have one at hand.

In CSMP programs, an initial and dynamic section are distinguishable. The equations that are needed to advance in time or to update the system at every time interval are in the dynamic section and the equations in the initial section define the invariable geometry of the system and provide the initial values.

The initial section begins with the lines:

```
INITIAL
NOSORT
```

The 'nosort' line means that the subsequent cards are given in order of computation, i.e. as an algorithm. In situations where arrays are handled, it is not possible to make use of the sorting capability of CSMP. This capability is used in Section 6.2 and in the paper on the simulation of the water flow in the soil-plant system by Lambert & Penning de Vries (1971).

The line:

```
PARAMETER TCOM = 2., COND = 86.4,
VHCAP = 0.25, ITMP = 20.
```

indicates that the thickness of the compartment is 2 cm, the thermal conductivity 86.4 cal cm$^{-1}$ day$^{-1}$ °C$^{-1}$, the volumetric heat capacity 0.25 cal cm$^{-3}$ °C$^{-1}$ and the initial temperature of the soil column 20 °C. Such comments may be entered on lines which start with an asterisk (*) in the first column.

The line:

```
FIXED I
```

states that there is a counter I which is used to perform the necessary calculations for all the compartments. This counter is at first used to obtain the initial volumetric heat contents for 25 compartments with the three FORTRAN statements:

```
DO 1 I = 1,25
IVHTC(I) = ITMP*TCOM*VHCAP
1 CONTINUE
```

In this way, IVHTC(1) is calculated for the first compartment, then I is increased by one and IVHTC(2) for the second compartment is calculated and so on, until IVHTC(25) for the last compartment. In this case 25 compartments are introduced which means, that the column is $25 \times 2 = 50$ cm.

This is the end of the initial section.

The dynamic section, in which all statements are given, that are necessary to calculate the flow rates at each time interval and to perform the integration, begins with:

```
DYNAMIC
NOSORT
```

The temperature of the 25 compartments is calculated from the volumetric heat content with:

```
DO 2 I = 1,25
TEMP(I) = VHTC(I)/(TCOM*VHCAP)
2 CONTINUE
```

The sinusoidal temperature variation at the surface is given by

```
TMPS = TAV + TAMPL * SIN (6.2832*TIME)
PARAMETER TAV=20., TAMPL=10.
```

in which TAV is the average temperature and TAMPL the amplitude of the temperature wave, both in degrees centigrade. The expression SIN calculates the sine of the argument, TIME is expressed in the same time units as are used for the transportcoefficient, i.e. days and

```
INITIAL
NOSORT
PARAMETER      TCOM = 2.,COND = 86.4,VHCAP = 0.25,ITMP = 20.
FIXED          I
       DO 1 I = 1,25
               IVHTC(I) = ITMP*TCOM*VHCAP
    1 CONTINUE
DYNAMIC
NOSORT
       DO 2 I = 1,25
               TEMP(I) = VHTC(I)/(TCOM*VHCAP)
    2 CONTINUE
               TMPS = TAV+TAMPL*SIN(6.2832*TIME)
PARAMETER      TAV = 20.,TAMPL = 10.
               FLOW(1) = (TMPS-TEMP(1))*COND/(0.5*TCOM)
       DO 3 I = 2,25
               FLOW(I) = (TEMP(I-1)-TEMP(I))*COND/TCOM
    3 CONTINUE
               FLOW(26) = 0.
       DO 4 I = 1,25
               NFLOW(I) = FLOW(I)-FLOW(I+1)
    4 CONTINUE
               VHTC1 = INTGRL(IVHTC1,NFLOW1,25)
/      EQUIVALENCE (IVHTC1,IVHTC(1)),(VHTC1,VHTC(1)),(NFLOW1,NFLOW(1))
/      REAL    TEMP(25),NFLOW(25),FLOW(26),IVHTC(25),VHTC(25)
METHOD         RECT
               T1 = TEMP(1)
PRTPLT         T1(10.,30.)
               T5 = TEMP(5)
PRTPLT         T5(10.,30.)
               T15 = TEMP(15)
PRTPLT         T15(10.,30.)
TIMER          FINTIM = 4.,DELT = 0.005, OUTDEL = 0.04
END
PARAMETER   .  TAV = 10.,TAMPL = 0.
END
STOP
```

Fig. 4a | C SMP program for the flow of heat in a homogeneous soil column.

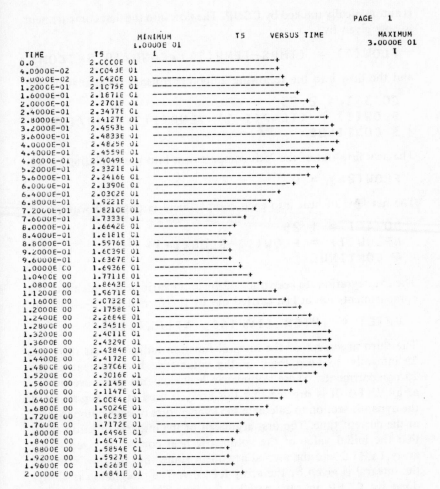

|  |  | MINIMUM<br>1.0000E 01 | T5 | VERSUS TIME | MAXIMUM<br>3.0000E 01 |
|---|---|---|---|---|---|
| TIME | T5 | I |  |  | I |
| 0.0 | 2.0000E 01 | ------------------------+ | | | |
| 4.0000E-02 | 2.0043E 01 | ------------------------+ | | | |
| 8.0000E-02 | 2.0420E 01 | -------------------------+ | | | |
| 1.2000E-01 | 2.1075E 01 | --------------------------+ | | | |
| 1.6000E-01 | 2.1871E 01 | ---------------------------+ | | | |
| 2.0000E-01 | 2.2701E 01 | -----------------------------+ | | | |
| 2.4000E-01 | 2.3477E 01 | ------------------------------+ | | | |
| 2.8000E-01 | 2.4127E 01 | -------------------------------+ | | | |
| 3.2000E-01 | 2.4593E 01 | --------------------------------+ | | | |
| 3.6000E-01 | 2.4833E 01 | --------------------------------+ | | | |
| 4.0000E-01 | 2.4825E 01 | --------------------------------+ | | | |
| 4.4000E-01 | 2.4559E 01 | --------------------------------+ | | | |
| 4.8000E-01 | 2.4049E 01 | -------------------------------+ | | | |
| 5.2000E-01 | 2.3321E 01 | ------------------------------+ | | | |
| 5.6000E-01 | 2.2416E 01 | ----------------------------+ | | | |
| 6.0000E-01 | 2.1390E 01 | --------------------------+ | | | |
| 6.4000E-01 | 2.0302E 01 | ------------------------+ | | | |
| 6.8000E-01 | 1.9221E 01 | ----------------------+ | | | |
| 7.2000E-01 | 1.8210E 01 | --------------------+ | | | |
| 7.6000E-01 | 1.7333E 01 | -------------------+ | | | |
| 8.0000E-01 | 1.6642E 01 | -----------------+ | | | |
| 8.4000E-01 | 1.6181E 01 | ----------------+ | | | |
| 8.8000E-01 | 1.5976E 01 | ---------------+ | | | |
| 9.2000E-01 | 1.6039E 01 | ---------------+ | | | |
| 9.6000E-01 | 1.6367E 01 | ----------------+ | | | |
| 1.0000E 00 | 1.6936E 01 | -----------------+ | | | |
| 1.0400E 00 | 1.7711E 01 | -------------------+ | | | |
| 1.0800E 00 | 1.8643E 01 | ---------------------+ | | | |
| 1.1200E 00 | 1.9671E 01 | ------------------------+ | | | |
| 1.1600E 00 | 2.0732E 01 | --------------------------+ | | | |
| 1.2000E 00 | 2.1758E 01 | ---------------------------+ | | | |
| 1.2400E 00 | 2.2684E 01 | ----------------------------+ | | | |
| 1.2800E 00 | 2.3451E 01 | ------------------------------+ | | | |
| 1.3200E 00 | 2.4011E 01 | -------------------------------+ | | | |
| 1.3600E 00 | 2.4329E 01 | -------------------------------+ | | | |
| 1.4000E 00 | 2.4384E 01 | --------------------------------+ | | | |
| 1.4400E 00 | 2.4172E 01 | -------------------------------+ | | | |
| 1.4800E 00 | 2.3706E 01 | ------------------------------+ | | | |
| 1.5200E 00 | 2.3016E 01 | -----------------------------+ | | | |
| 1.5600E 00 | 2.2145E 01 | ---------------------------+ | | | |
| 1.6000E 00 | 2.1147E 01 | -------------------------+ | | | |
| 1.6400E 00 | 2.0064E 01 | ------------------------+ | | | |
| 1.6800E 00 | 1.9024E 01 | ----------------------+ | | | |
| 1.7200E 00 | 1.8033E 01 | --------------------+ | | | |
| 1.7600E 00 | 1.7172E 01 | -------------------+ | | | |
| 1.8000E 00 | 1.6496E 01 | -----------------+ | | | |
| 1.8400E 00 | 1.6047E 01 | ----------------+ | | | |
| 1.8800E 00 | 1.5854E 01 | ---------------+ | | | |
| 1.9200E 00 | 1.5927E 01 | ---------------+ | | | |
| 1.9600E 00 | 1.6263E 01 | ----------------+ | | | |
| 2.0000E 00 | 1.6841E 01 | -----------------+ | | | |

Fig. 4b | Part of the generated print-plot (PRTPLT) output of the CSMP program from Fig. 4a.

11

is automatically tracked by CSMP. The flow into the first compartment is now given by

```
FLOW(1) = (TMPS-TEMP(1))*COND/(0.5*TCOM)
```

and the flow into the following 24 compartments is calculated with

```
DO 3 I = 2,25
FLOW(I) = (TEMP(I-1)-TEMP(I))*COND/TCOM
3 CONTINUE
```

The heat flow out of the 25th compartment into the insulating layer is

```
FLOW(26) = 0.
```

The net flow of heat into each compartment is obtained with

```
DO 4 I = 1,25
NFLOW(I) = FLOW(I)-FLOW(I+1)
4 CONTINUE
```

The 25 integrations to keep track of the volumetric heat contents of the compartments are at last carried out by the formal CSMP function:

```
VHTC1 = INTGRL(IVHTC1, NFLOW1,25)
```

The third argument of the integral function indicates that there are 25 integrals, to keep track of the volumetric heat content of the 25 compartments. These volumetric heat contents are stored in an array VHTC. It is stressed that this array is used at the beginning of the dynamic section to calculate the temperature of each compartment at the current time. The first argument of the integral function states that the initial value of the volumetric heat content is given by an array IVHTC and the second argument states that the flow rate into the integral is given by the array NFLOW. The integration is always done by CSMP in semi-parallel fashion. This means that at the current time *all* flow rates are calculated from the state of the system, and that after this *all* integrations are performed.

Now the arrays must be 'declared' and 'located'.
This is done as follows:

```
/ REAL TEMP(25), FLOW(26), NFLOW(25),
VHTC(25), IVHTC(25)
/ EQUIVALENCE (IVHTC1,IVHTC(1)),(VHTC1,
VHTC(1)),(NFLOW1,NFLOW(1))
```

The two statements beginning with a slash (/) in the first column organise the memory of the computer and one should not attempt to understand them at an early stage of the game without some reasonable knowledge of FORTRAN.

If the integration is to be carried out according to the simple rectlinear method, as is suggested in the previous section, the line:

```
METHOD RECT
```

is entered. However, it will appear that it is better to use one of the more sophisticated methods of integration that are available in CSMP. To obtain a graph of the temperature of the first, fifth and fifteenth compartment the lines:

```
T1 = TEMP(1)
PRTPLT T1 (10.,30.)
T5 = TEMP(5)
PRTPLT T5 (10.,30.)
T15 = TEMP (15)
PRTPLT T15(10.,30.)
```

have to be entered. The numbers in brackets on the PRinTPLoT cards provide the scale of the dependent variable. CSMP chooses its own scale if these figures are not provided. The independent variable is time, provided by CSMP.

The necessary line:

```
TIMER FINTIM=4., DELT=0.005, OUTDEL=0.04
```

means that the calculation has to be done for 4 days (FINTIM), that the machine has to advance in time intervals of 0.005 day (DELT) and that the dependent variable of the plots is given in intervals of 0.04 day (OUTDEL).

Now the program and the first run are ended by the line:

```
END
```

By introducing here the statement:

```
PARAMETER TAV=10., TAMPL=0.
```

the calculation is repeated with these parameter values. These indicate that at time zero the temperature of the surface is decreased from 20°C to 10°C and maintained there, as may be verified by inspection of the expression for the temperature of the surface (TMPS) in the program.

This run is also concluded with

END

and if at this stage no more calculations are necessary, the whole program is to be completed by the word:

STOP

A reproduction of the program as punched for cards and a part of the output is given in Figs 4a and 4b (p. 10 and 11).

## 2.3 Time constant and methods of integration

The system of integration, used in the previous example, is the simplest method of centralized, forward integration. At any instant of time, the volumetric heat contents of all boxes and the boundary conditions at the top and bottom of the soil column are given. These are used to calculate, independently of each other, the net flow rates at this instant of time, which are then used to update all volumetric heat contents over a small time interval. In this way, the integration is done in a semi-parallel fashion. Since all flow rates are calculated independently of each other, this system of explicit integration may be extended conveniently to much more complicated systems, as will be shown later. Unfortunately the time intervals are shorter than with implicit methods, in which actual changes over a certain time interval are calculated by matrix methods. However, this disadvantage is often more than offset by the simplicity of programming and the fewer actual arithmetical operations at each step.

In the example a time interval (DELT) of 0.005 days was used. The calculation may oscillate with larger time intervals and computer time is wasted with smaller time intervals. The simplest way to find the correct time interval is to run the system with values for DELT a factor 2–10 apart and to make a graph of the temperature in one of the top compartments against DELT as is done in Fig. 5. A sharp transition zone can usually be seen between the range where the system oscillates and the correct range.

A first estimate of DELT may be obtained by considering the heat content of the first compartment and the rate of change at the onset

14

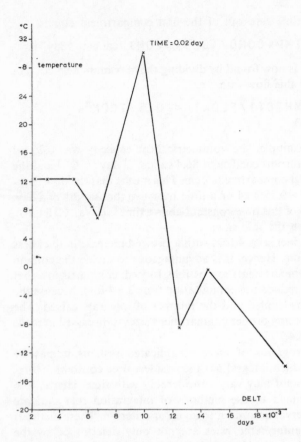

Fig. 5 | The temperature of the first compartment at 0.02 day, calculated with different time intervals (DELT).

of the temperature drop. There is an oscillation when during the first time interval so much heat is taken out of the first compartment that its temperature drops below the new temperature of the surface. In a simulation, where the temperature at the surface suddenly drops with a value DTMP, the maximum heat content that could be removed from the first compartment equals

$$MHTCT1 = DTMP*VHCAP*TCOM \quad cal\,cm^{-2}$$

15

The flow rate at time zero out of the first compartment equals

FLOW1 = DTMP*COND/(0.5*TCOM) cal cm$^{-2}$day$^{-1}$

The time constant is now found by dividing the maximum heat content to be removed by this flow rate, i.e.:

TMCNST = MHTCT1/FLOW1 = 0.5*TCOM$^2$*
VHCAP/COND

In the previous example, the volumetric heat capacity was 0.25 cal cm$^{-3}$°C$^{-1}$, the transport coefficient 86.4 cal cm$^{-1}$ day$^{-1}$°C$^{-1}$ and the thickness of the first compartment 2 cm. This means that the time constant equals 0.5*2$^2$ × 0.25/86.4 or a little over five thousandth of a day. A value of about $\frac{1}{4}$ of this time constant gives a time interval (DELT), which is usually on the safe side.

The time constant increases 4-fold with a twofold increase in thickness of the compartments. Hence, it is advantageous to divide the column up into as large compartments as possible. Indeed, compartments that are twice as large reduce the computation time 2 × 4-fold, because the time interval is quadrupled and the number of integrals halved. The importance of choosing proper compartment sizes is discussed in more detail in Section 6.4.

For simulation programs of more complicated systems it may be difficult to judge which integral has the smallest time constant. Moreover the time constant may vary considerably with time. Hence, it is often more convenient to use methods of integration that evaluate their own time interval according to an error criterion. These methods also have an advantage: the rates are not only determined by the current values of the integrals, but their change with time is also taken into account.

The Milne fifth order predictor-corrector method, available in CSMP, is often a good choice for distributive systems. This method is described in detail by Milne (1960), but to give some idea of the mathematics involved, the actual procedure of computation, as described in the CSMP Manual, will be given here.

At first the value of the integral ($Y$) for the current time ($t$) plus a finite time interval ($\Delta t$) is predicted by means of

$$YP_{t+\Delta t} = Y_{t-\Delta t} + \frac{\Delta t}{3}(8.X_t - 5.X_{t-\Delta t} + 4.X_{t-2\Delta t} - X_{t-3\Delta t})$$

in which $X_t$, $X_{t-\Delta t}$, $X_{t-2\Delta t}$ and $X_{t-3\Delta t}$ are the rates of change of the integral at the current time and at time $\Delta t$, $2.\Delta t$ and $3.\Delta t$ in the past. With the predicted values of this integral i.e. $YP_{t+\Delta t}$ and all other integrals of the problem involved, the rate of change at the time $t+\Delta t$ (i.e. $X_{t+\Delta t}$) is predicted. This prediction is used to calculate a corrector for the value of the integral at time $t+\Delta t$ with:

$$YC_{t+\Delta t} = \tfrac{1}{8}(Y_t + 7.Y_{t-\Delta t}) +$$

$$+ \frac{\Delta t}{192}(65.X_{t+\Delta t} + 243.X_t + 51.X_{t-\Delta t} + X_{t-2\Delta t})$$

Then the actual value of $Y_{t+\Delta t}$ is obtained by a weighted average of predictor and corrector, according to:

$$Y_{t+\Delta t} = 0.96116 * YC_{t+\Delta t} + 0.03884 * YP_{t+\Delta t}$$

The time interval is adjusted at such a small value that for an absolute value of $YC$ greater than 1:

$$\frac{0.04\,|YC-YP|}{R \times |YC|} \leqslant 1$$

and for an absolute value of $YC$ smaller or equal to 1:

$$\frac{0.04\,|YC-YP|}{R} \leqslant 1$$

The value of $R$ is set by C S M P at 0.0001, but may be specified by the user at some other value. If the predicted and corrected values of one of the integrals are so far apart that the above criteria are not met, C S M P decreases the time interval with a factor two and tries again. For very rapid changes, it may be impossible to find a small enough time interval to satisfy the error criterion because the numbers in a digital machine are of finite length. Then the computation is terminated. If on the other hand, the error criterion is met, C S M P increases the next time interval twofold.

Another integration routine with variable time interval provided by C S M P is based on the fourth order method of Runge-Kutta (R K S). Here the new values of the integrals are not based on past values of the

17

rates but on the present rate and three rates between $t$ and a maximum $\Delta t$ in the future. This method, also described by Milne (1960) and in the Manual, may be the most reliable, but often takes considerable computation time.

By inserting the line:

METHOD MILNE

or

METHOD RKS

instead of the line:

METHOD RECT

in the simulation program, CSMP chooses the indicated integration method.

Other methods of integration: the Adams second order, the Simpson, the trapezoidal and the Runge Kutta fourth order method with fixed time interval, are also provided by CSMP, described in the Manual, and discussed more thoroughly by Milne. They are of little additional use for solving distributive systems.

## 2.4 Influence of a sand cover on temperature regime of a peat soil

De Vries & de Wit (1954) analysed the influence of a layer of sand on a peat soil on the daily temperature amplitude at the soil surface and thus on decreasing the risk of night-frosts. For an analytical solution, it is necessary to assume that both the thermal properties of the sand and the peat are a constant function of depth and that the exchange of energy between the soil and its surroundings varied sinusoidal with time and is independent of the temperature amplitude at the soil surface. However, the sensible heat exchange between the surface of the soil and the air and the long wave radiation loss depend to a considerable extent on the temperature at the surface, so that the nightly drop in temperature in its turn may be affected. Since the risk of night-frost depends on small differences in temperature, it may be worthwhile to analyse the problem by a simulation program in which these effects are included, and which may account for changing properties of the soil with depth.

The main features of such a program are given here as an illustration

18

of how more complicated problems are handled by simulation. Since the transport of water will be discussed in a later section, the influence of evaporation and the resulting water movement in the soil on the heat budget has not been included in the analyses at this stage.

The soil surface exchanges heat with its surroundings in various ways. Depending on conditions, it gains or loses heat from the underlying soil and gains heat generated by the absorption of the radiation from sun and sky. It also loses heat by long wave radiation towards the sky and by sensible heat exchange with the adjacent air.

The sensible heat exchange of the surface is proportional to the difference in temperature between the soil surface and the air:

$$SHL = HEC*(TMPS-TMPA) \quad cal\,cm^{-2}hr^{-1}$$

The proportionality factor is the heat exchange coefficient. Penman (1948) used the expression:

$$HEC = 0.42*(1+0.5*WS) \quad cal\,cm^{-2}hr^{-1}{}^{\circ}C^{-1}$$

to estimate the heat exchange coefficient. Windspeed in $m\,sec^{-1}$ and temperature of the air are measured at screen height.

The long wave radiation loss may be estimated by the expression of Brunt (1932):

$$LWR = 4.91*10^{-9}*(273+TMPS)^4*(0.56-0.092\sqrt{VPA})*(0.10+0.9*FBRGT) \quad cal\,cm^{-2}hr^{-1}$$

in which VPA is the vapour pressure of the air in mm Hg at screen height and FBRGT is the fraction of the sky that is bright. The numerical values in this semi-experimental formula are obtained from an analysis of experimental data assuming that the temperature of the air is measured close to the soil surface. Without a critical analysis, the formula is used here with the temperature of the soil surface and applied for shorter periods of time than intended. The short wave radiation is absorbed in the top few millimeters of the soil. Since we are interested in the temperature of the surface, the top compartment cannot be larger than about 0.5 cm. As the daily fluctuation of temperature decreases with increasing depth, the size of the compartments may be increased as depth increases. By taking a thickness of $0.5, 4 \times 1., 1.5$ and $3 \times 2.$ cm for the first nine compartments, the depth is well below the layer of sand. From then on the size of the compartments may be increased by 1 cm, so that with a total of 20 compartments a depth of 100 cm below the surface is reached. The daily fluctuation of temperature is negligible at this depth.

To avoid introduction of evaporation and condensation at this stage, it is assumed that the air and the top 6 cm of soil are dry, be it peat or sand, and that from thereon the moisture content of the soil increases gradually until at 100 cm saturation is reached. The data for the thermal conductivity and volumetric heat capacity of the sand and peat at different moisture contents are taken from de Vries & de Wit (1954). The transfer of heat due to flow of water in the soil is not taken into account in this stage.

The programming is again straightforward.

```
INITIAL
NOSORT
```

At first, the thicknesses of the successive compartments are given in the form of a table:

```
STORAGE TCOM(20)
TCOM(1-20) = 0.5,4*1.,1.5,3*2.,3.,4.,5.,
6.,7.,8.,9.,10.,11.,12.,13.
```

The STORAGE statement is necessary to reserve memory space for tabled variables. Then a counter is defined to use in the calculation with

```
FIXED I
```

and the depth of the centre of each compartment below the surface and the distance between the centres of two consecutive compartments are calculated with

```
DEPTH(1) = 0.5*TCOM(1)
DIST(1)  = 0.5*TCOM(1)
```

and

```
DO 1 I = 2,20
DIST(I) = 0.5*(TCOM(I)+TCOM(I-1))
DEPTH(I) = DEPTH(I-1) + DIST (I)
1 CONTINUE
```

The FORTRAN output capability may be used to print the answers of this calculation:

```
WRITE(6,100) DEPTH
100 FORMAT (1Hb,5HDEPTH//(10F10.4))
```

The number 6 refers to the tape, which is used by the machine and
the number 100 specifies that the FORMAT statement with number
100 organizes the layout of the writing. In this format, 1 H b(lank),
indicates that a new page is taken, then the title is written with
5HDEPTH. The two slashes (//) introduce two blank lines, before
the depths of the successive compartments are written according to
10 F10.4, i.e. with a maximum of 10 in a row, reserving ten spaces
for the number of which four are after the decimal point.
The generated output is given in Fig. 6, (p. 23) as an example.
The value of the conductivity dependent on depth is introduced as a
tabulated function in which the first of each pair of numbers is the
independent variable (depth in cm) and the second of each pair the
dependent variable (conductivity in cal $cm^{-1}hr^{-1}°C^{-1}$), as follows:

```
FUNCTION CONTBL = (0.,0.288),(6.,0.288),
(8.,2.484),(10.,2.498),(12.,2.506),
(14.,2.513),(18.,2.527),(22.,2.538),
(28.,2.545),(34.,2.592),(42.,2.657),
(50.,2.7),(60.,2.765),(70.,3.132),
(80.,3.218),(90.,4.104),(100.,4.284)
```

Similary the value of the volumetric heat capacity in cal $cm^{-3}°C^{-1}$,
dependent on depth in cm, is given by

```
FUNCTION VHCPTB = (0.,.06),(6.,.06),
(8.,.57),(10.,.573),(12.,.575),
(14.,.577),(18.,.58),(22.,.583),
(28.,.585),(34.,.6),(42.,.615),
(50.,.625),(60.,.64),(70.,.72),
(80.,.74),(90.,.90),(100.,.97)
```

These two tabulated functions specify possible thermal properties of
a peat soil without sand cover and with a moisture content that from
6 cm on increases with depth. The values of the conductivity and
volumetric heat capacity at the centre of each compartment are now
calculated as follows:

21

```
DO 2 I = 1,20
COND(I) = AFGEN(CONTBL,DEPTH(I))
VHCAP(I) = AFGEN(VHCPTB,DEPTH(I))
2 CONTINUE
```

The AFGEN function is a CSMP function, which interpolates linearly in the tabulated function defined by the first name in the argument, using the second name in the argument as the independent variable. The average conductivity from the centre of one compartment to the centre of the following one is calculated with

```
DO 3 I = 2,20
AVCND(I) = (TCOM(I-1)+TCOM(I))/
(TCOM(I-1)/COND(I-1)+TCOM(I)/COND(I))
3 CONTINUE
```

Large equations, written in FORTRAN, need some deciphering: the averaging of the conductivities is done here, in the same way as for electrical conductivities. Instead of averaging the conductivities between the compartments, it would have been possible to use a table with conductivities at the boundary of each compartment. It is a good exercise to write the program according to this suggestion.

The initial temperature of the 20 compartments is again given in a table:

```
STORAGE ITMP(20)
TABLE ITMP(1-20) = 20 * 4.5
```

This means that all 20 compartments have the same initial temperature for which the average air temperature is choosen as a first guess. The initial volumetric heat content of the compartments is now obtained with

```
DO 4 I = 1,20
IVHTC(I) = ITMP(I)*VHCAP(I)*TCOM(I)
4 CONTINUE
```

Here the initialization is complete, so that the program may be continued with the dynamic section:

```
DYNAMIC
NOSORT
```

The temperatures of the 20 compartments are again calculated with

DEPTH

| 0.2500 | 1.0000 | 2.0000 | 3.0000 | 4.0000 | 5.2500 | 7.0000 | 9.0000 | 11.0000 | 13.5000 |
| 17.0000 | 21.500C | 27.0000 | 33.5000 | 41.0000 | 49.5000 | 59.0000 | 69.5000 | 81.0000 | 93.5000 |

Fig. 6| The generated FORTRAN output, according to FORMAT statement 100.

HEAT FLOW IN LAYERED SOILS, WHOLE PROFILE CONSISTS OUT OF SAND    MILNE INTEGRATION

TIME = 9.0000E 00

```
TEMP1  = 5.1194E 00    TEMP2  = 4.0125E 00    TEMP3  = 3.0125E 00    TEMP4  = 2.3882E 00
TEMP5  = 2.0508E 00    TEMP6  = 1.8882E 00    TEMP7  = 1.9330E 00    TEMP8  = 2.0102E 00
TEMP9  = 2.1314E 00    TEMP10 = 2.3212E 00    TEMP11 = 2.6316E 00    TEMP12 = 3.0451E 00
TEMP14 = 3.9046E 00    TEMP15 = 4.2014E 00    TEMP16 = 4.3758E 00    TEMP17 = 4.4574E 00
TEMP18 = 4.4875E 00    TEMP19 = 4.4963E 00    TELLER = 7.0500E 02    DELT   = 3.1250E-02
```

TIME = 1.0000E 01

```
TEMP1  = 1.0582E 01    TEMP2  = 8.6223E 00    TEMP3  = 6.6291E 00    TEMP4  = 5.1460E 00
TEMP5  = 4.0578E 00    TEMP6  = 3.0651E 00    TEMP7  = 2.5778E 00    TEMP8  = 2.4033E 00
TEMP9  = 2.4831E 00    TEMP10 = 2.5398E 00    TEMP11 = 2.7158E 00    TEMP12 = 3.0221E 00
TEMP14 = 3.8065E 00    TEMP15 = 4.1238E 00    TEMP16 = 4.3296E 00    TEMP17 = 4.4360E 00
TEMP18 = 4.4798E 00    TEMP19 = 4.4940E 00    TELLER = 7.6600E 02    DELT   = 6.2500E-02
```

TIME = 1.1000E 01

```
TEMP1  = 1.6319E 01    TEMP2  = 1.3689E 01    TEMP3  = 1.0825E 01    TEMP4  = 8.4983E 00
TEMP5  = 6.6071E 00    TEMP6  = 4.6644E 00    TEMP7  = 3.5349E 00    TEMP8  = 3.2471E 00
TEMP9  = 3.0661E 00    TEMP10 = 2.9457E 00    TEMP11 = 2.9383E 00    TEMP12 = 3.0926E 00
TEMP14 = 3.7353E 00    TEMP15 = 4.0534E 00    TEMP16 = 4.2811E 00    TEMP17 = 4.4108E 00
TEMP18 = 4.4996E 00    TEMP19 = 4.4907E 00    TELLER = 8.3900E 02    DELT   = 1.5625E-02
```

TIME = 1.2000E 01

```
TEMP1  = 1.8090E 01    TEMP2  = 1.6047E 01    TEMP3  = 1.3457E 01    TEMP4  = 1.1047E 01
TEMP5  = 8.8334E 00    TEMP6  = 6.3104E 00    TEMP7  = 4.6856E 00    TEMP8  = 4.2143E 00
TEMP9  = 3.8612E 00    TEMP10 = 3.5472E 00    TEMP11 = 3.3207E 00    TEMP12 = 3.2772E 00
TEMP14 = 3.7008E 00    TEMP15 = 3.9966E 00    TEMP16 = 4.2340E 00    TEMP17 = 4.3829E 00
TEMP18 = 4.4569E 00    TEMP19 = 4.4861E 00    TELLER = 9.1700E 02    DELT   = 3.1250E-02
```

Fig. 7| Part of the output, generated with the PRINT capability.

```
DO 5 I = 1,20
TMP(I) = VHTC(I)/(TCOM(I)*VHCAP(I))
5 CONTINUE
```

and the flow of heat from one compartment to the next one with

```
DO 6 I = 2,20
FLOW(I) = (TMP(I-1)-TMP(I))*AVCND(I)/
DIST(I)
6 CONTINUE
```

The flow out of the 20th compartment is again given by

```
FLOW(21) = 0.
```

because temperature variations at this depth are negligible.
In the next part of the program, the exchange of heat between the first compartment and the atmosphere is considered. For this purpose the short wave radiation, the long wave radiation and the sensible heat exchange have to be calculated.
The short wave radiation is given as a tabulated function, a bright day being choosen at the end of April in the Netherlands:

```
FUNCTION SWRTB = (0.,0.),(5.,0.),
(6.,3.32),(7.,10.78),(8.,14.93),
(9.,25.71),(10.,39.81),(11.,52.25),
(12.,48.93),(13.,51.42),(14.,31.51),
(15.,27.37),(16.,18.24),(17.,8.29),
(18.,.83),(19.,0.),(24.,0.)
```

with the independent variable in hours and the dependent variable in cal cm$^{-2}$hr$^{-1}$.
In order to allow time for the development of a stationary situation, it may be necessary to operate the simulation program for more than one day. To avoid introducing experimental data for a longer period, it is assumed that the chosen day repeats itself. For this purpose the tabulated function is not read with time itself, but with DTIME, defined as:

```
DTIME = AMOD(TIME,24.)
```

This function makes at the first day DTIME equal to TIME, at the second day equal to TIME-24, at the third day equal to TIME-48, and so on, hence introduces the required repetition. Now the short wave radiation at any time of the day is obtained with

```
SWR = AFGEN(SWRTB,DTIME)
```

Some radiation is reflected, so that the absorbed short wave radiation equals

```
ASWR = ABSC*SWR
```

in which ABSC, the absorption coefficient for short wave radiation, is given by

```
PARAMETER ABSC = 0.9
```

for dark peat soils.
For the calculation of the long wave radiation, the fraction of the sky that is bright and the vapour pressure of the air at screen height (in mm Hg) are needed. Under conditions where night-frosts occur, the daily variation of both weather parameters may be small, so that these are introduced as constants with

```
PARAMETER VPA = 5., FBRGT = 0.95
```

Hence, it is supposed that the air is dry and the sky is clear: conditions that favour large temperature fluctuations at the soil surface. The long wave radiation is now calculated with

```
LWR = 4.91E-9*(TMPS+273)**4*
(.56-.092*SQRT(VPA))*(.10+0.9*FBRGT)
```

expressed in cal cm$^{-2}$hr$^{-1}$, E–9 standing for $10^{-9}$, and SQRT being a FORTRAN function, that provides the square root of the argument. To calculate the sensible heat loss, the heat exchange coefficient is needed, which depends on the wind speed. The assumption that the wind speed during the day hours is 3 m s$^{-1}$ and during the night 0.5 m s$^{-1}$ is again introduced with a tabulated function:

```
FUNCTION WSTBL = (0.,0.5),(5.,0.5),
(5.1,3.0),(19.,3.0),(19.1,0.5),(24.,0.5)
```

in hours and m sec$^{-1}$, respectively. This table is read again with DTIME, defined before:

```
WS = AFGEN(WSTBL,DTIME)
```

The heat exchange coefficient is now given with

$$HEC = 0.42*(1+0.5*WS) \quad \text{in cal}\,\text{cm}^{-2}\text{hr}^{-1}\,°\text{C}^{-1}$$

Now, the temperature of the air is tabulated, for a bright day at the end of April:

```
FUNCTION TMPATB = (0.,1.3),(1.,1.9),
(2.,0.7),(3.,-0.3),(4.,-0.1),(5.,0.5),
(6.,0.7),(7.,2.0),(8.,2.8),(9.,3.5),
(10.,4.2),(11.,5.5),(12.,7.2),(13.,8.2),
(14.,8.8),(15.,9.0),(16.,9.1),(17.,9.0),
(18.,8.0),(19.,6.5),(20.,4.8),(21.,3.9),
(22.,3.8),(23.,3.0),(24.,1.3).
```

in hours and °C, respectively. This table is read with

```
TMPA = AFGEN(TMPATB,DTIME)
```

At last the sensible heat loss can be calculated with

```
SHL = (TMP(1)-TMPA)*HEC
```

in which the temperature of the first thin compartment is substituted for the temperature at the surface.

The flow of heat from the atmosphere towards the soil is then given by

```
FLOW(1) = ASWR-SHL-LWR
```

We may proceed with calculating the net flow of heat into each compartment with

```
DO 7 I = 1,20
NFLW(I) = FLOW(I)-FLOW(I+1)
7 CONTINUE
```

The 20 integrations are finally carried out with the formal CSMP function:

```
VHTC1 = INTGRL(IVHTC1,NFLW1,20)
```

Now the arrays used have to be 'declared' and 'located' with

```
/ REAL DEPTH(20), COND(20),VHCAP(20),
AVCND(20), IVHTC(20), TMP(20),
/ REAL FLOW(21), NFLW(20), VHTC(20),
DIST(20).
/ EQUIVALENCE(VHTC1,VHTC(1)),(IVHTC1,
IVHTC(1)),(NFLW1,NFLW(1)).
```

This is also the time to check whether all units of the variables are consistent.
The integration is done by the method of Milne and the simulation run is at first, extended over a period of four days, answers being needed every hour. This is achieved with

```
METHOD MILNE
TIMER FINTIM=96., OUTDEL=1.
```

It should be noted that it is unnecessary to define the size of the time interval, when Milne's method is used for the integrations.
Since the temperature at the surface is of main interest, this temperature is plotted with

```
T1 = TMP(1)
PRTPLT T1
```

The scale is not specified, because the range is not known.
The temperature of the other 20 compartments may be printed by using the FORTRAN capability for printing arrays. If the PRINT routine of CSMP is used, which has the advantage of an organised layout, it is necessary to 'undimensionalize' the temperature with the statements:

```
T2 = TMP(2)
T3 = TMP(3)
  .
  .
  .
T20 = TMP(20)
```

and then to specify:

```
PRINT T1, T2, T3, ..............., T20.
```

Printing is then carried out at hourly intervals as specified by OUTDEL. An example of the layout is given in Fig. 7 (p. 23), where it may be noted that the time, provided by CSMP, is also printed.

Since some other runs have to be made, it is convenient to add title cards, the text of which is repeated on all pages with printed output:

```
TITLE HEAT FLOW IN LAYERED SOILS
TITLE WHOLE PROFILE CONSISTS OF
PEAT, ABSC = 0.9
```

This is then the

```
END
```

of the program and of the first run.

Other runs may be made: when the whole profile or the first 6, or the first 12 cm of the profile consists of sand and for various absorption coefficients at the surface. For this purpose, functions of the thermal properties of the profile have then to be redefined, and new title cards are added:

```
TITLE WHOLE PROFILE CONSISTS OF SAND,
ABSC = 0.9
FUNCTION CONTBL = (0.,2.160),
(5.9,2.160),(6.1,12.6),(100.,12.6)
FUNCTION VHCPTB = (0.,.27),(5.9,.27),
(6.1,.38),(100.,.38)
END
TITLE FIRST 6 CM OF PROFILE SAND,
FURTHER ON PEAT, ABSC = 0.9
FUNCTION CONTBL = (0.,2.160),
(5.9,2.160),(6.1,2.484),(8.,2.484), ...
FUNCTION VHCPTB = (0.,.27),(5.9,.27),
(6.1,.57),(8.,.57), ...
```

and so on, as in the tables for peat.

```
END
```

It may be prudent to simulate also the influence of a smaller absorption coefficient of the soil surface, which consists now of lighter coloured sand:

```
                    MINIMUM           TMPS  VERSUS TIME        MAXIMUM
                  -1.3052E 01         I                      3.6044E 01
  TIME      TMPS                I                                  I         TEMP2          TEMP4
```

| TIME | TMPS | TEMP2 | TEMP4 |
|---|---|---|---|
| 0.0 | 4.5000E 00 | 4.5000E 00 | 4.5000E 00 |
| 1.0000E 00 | -1.0705E 01 | -7.4913E 00 | -6.4981E-01 |
| 2.0000E 00 | -1.1970E 01 | -9.3171E 00 | -3.1272E 00 |
| 3.0000E 00 | -1.2906E 01 | -1.0399E 01 | -4.2954E 00 |
| 4.0000E 00 | -1.2950E 01 | -1.0728E 01 | -4.8950E 00 |
| 5.0000E 00 | -1.2592E 01 | -1.0580E 01 | -5.0697E 00 |
| 6.0000E 00 | -4.7140E 00 | -4.6707E 00 | -2.8253E 00 |
| 7.0000E 00 | 1.5621E 00 | 2.0465E-01 | -2.9521E-01 |
| 8.0000E 00 | 5.4796E 00 | 4.0410E 00 | 2.4270E 00 |
| 9.0000E 00 | 1.3457E 01 | 1.0188E 01 | 5.4348E 00 |
| 1.0000E 01 | 2.3435E 01 | 1.8621E 01 | 9.8880E 00 |
| 1.1000E 01 | 3.3668E 01 | 2.7251E 01 | 1.5152E 01 |
| 1.2000E 01 | 3.3649E 01 | 2.9477E 01 | 1.8746E 01 |
| 1.3000E 01 | 3.6044E 01 | 3.1380E 01 | 2.0232E 01 |
| 1.4000E 01 | 2.3962E 01 | 2.7417E 01 | 1.9119E 01 |
| 1.5000E 01 | 2.0500E 01 | 1.9685E 01 | 1.5669E 01 |
| 1.6000E 01 | 1.4324E 01 | 1.4815E 01 | 1.3035E 01 |
| 1.7000E 01 | 7.1762E 00 | 8.8540E 00 | 9.7391E 00 |
| 1.8000E 01 | 8.5003E-01 | 3.1923E 00 | 6.1005E 00 |
| 1.9000E 01 | -1.4336E 00 | 2.6589E-01 | 3.4549E 00 |
| 2.0000E 01 | -8.5419E 00 | -5.7321E 00 | 1.2890E-01 |
| 2.1000E 01 | -9.5842E 00 | -7.2571E 00 | -1.7565E 00 |
| 2.2000E 01 | -9.8671E 00 | -7.8239E 00 | -2.6166E 00 |
| 2.3000E 01 | -1.0458E 01 | -8.3562E 00 | -3.0965E 00 |
| 2.4000E 01 | -1.1662E 01 | -9.3062E 00 | -3.6522E 00 |
| 2.5000E 01 | -1.1473E 01 | -9.4742E 00 | -4.1048E 00 |
| 2.6000E 01 | -1.2226E 01 | -9.9774E 00 | -4.3737E 00 |
| 2.7000E 01 | -1.3005E 01 | -1.0661E 01 | -4.8726E 00 |
| 2.8000E 01 | -1.2999E 01 | -1.0854E 01 | -5.1675E 00 |
| 2.9000E 01 | -1.2618E 01 | -1.0655E 01 | -5.2406E 00 |
| 3.0000E 01 | -4.7248E 00 | -4.7146E 00 | -2.9454E 00 |
| 3.1000E 01 | 1.5536E 00 | 1.7157E-01 | -3.8866E-01 |
| 3.2000E 01 | 5.4730E 00 | 4.0540E 00 | 2.3497E 00 |
| 3.3000E 01 | 1.3451E 01 | 1.0165E 01 | 5.3698E 00 |
| 3.4000E 01 | 2.3824E 01 | 1.8602E 01 | 9.8302E 00 |
| 3.5000E 01 | 3.3666E 01 | 2.7233E 01 | 1.5101E 01 |
| 3.6000E 01 | 3.3644E 01 | 2.9442E 01 | 1.8700E 01 |
| 3.7000E 01 | 3.6041E 01 | 3.1366E 01 | 2.0190E 01 |
| 3.8000E 01 | 2.3958E 01 | 2.4161E 01 | 1.9081E 01 |
| 3.9000E 01 | 2.0497E 01 | 1.9673E 01 | 1.5634E 01 |
| 4.0000E 01 | 1.4321E 01 | 1.4804E 01 | 1.3002E 01 |
| 4.1000E 01 | 7.1736E 00 | 8.8437E 00 | 9.7043E 00 |
| 4.2000E 01 | 8.4765E-01 | 3.1825E 00 | 6.1616E 00 |
| 4.3000E 01 | -1.4357E 00 | 2.5667E-01 | 3.4296E 00 |
| 4.4000E 01 | -8.5454E 00 | -5.7421E 00 | 1.0259E-01 |
| 4.5000E 01 | -9.5878E 00 | -7.2666E 00 | -1.7807E 00 |
| 4.6000E 01 | -9.8705E 00 | -7.8331E 00 | -2.6407E 00 |
| 4.7000E 01 | -1.0461E 01 | -8.3650E 00 | -3.1196E 00 |
| 4.8000E 01 | -1.1666E 01 | -9.3146E 00 | -3.6744E 00 |
| 4.9000E 01 | -1.1476E 01 | -9.4823E 00 | -4.1302E 00 |
| 5.0000E 01 | -1.2229E 01 | -9.9852E 00 | -4.3942E 00 |

Fig. 8| Part of the output, generated with the print-plot (PRTPLT) routine.

```
PARAMETER ABSC = 0.6
END
TITLE FIRST 12 CM OF PROFILE SAND,
FURTHER ON PEAT, FIRST 6 CM DRY,
ABSC = 0.6
FUNCTION VHCPTB = (0.,.27),(6.,.27),
(6.1,.3.35),(10.,.380),(11.9,.380),
(12.1,.575), ...
FUNCTION CONTBL = (0.,2.160),(5.9,2.160),
(6.1,12.6),(8.,12.6),(10.,12.6),
(11.9,12.6),(12.1,2.506), ...
```

and so on, as in the tables for peat.

29

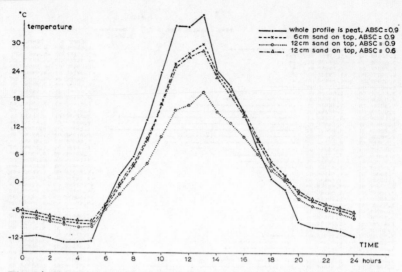

Fig. 9 | The variation of the temperature of the first 0.5 cm of the soil on the fourth day for various soil conditions.

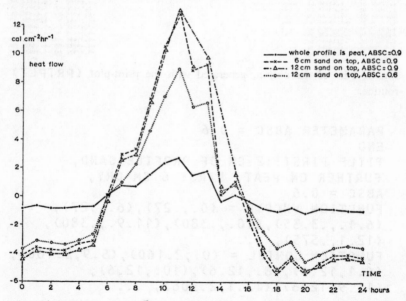

Fig. 10 | Heat flow from the air to the soil on the fourth day for various soil conditions.

30

```
END
TITLE FIRST 12 CM OF PROFILE SAND,
FURTHER ON PEAT, ABSC = 0.9
PARAMETER ABSC = 0.9
END
STOP
```

A print-plotted output is reproduced in Fig. 8. In Fig. 9 the temperature of the first compartment of 0.5 cm is given for the fourth day and for all profiles. It appears that the layer of sand, considerably reduces the temperature drop at night, mainly because of a higher conductivity and volumetric heat capacity than peat. The effect is still greater when black sand is used, as is illustrated by the result of a run with 12 cm sand and an absorption coefficient of 0.9. The heat flow into the soil during the day and out of the soil during the night for the profiles is given in Fig. 10. In accordance with Fig. 9 for the temperature, it appears that the heat exchange with the underlying soil is much higher on the sand than on the peat soil.

It is impossible to find an analytical solution for the problem which has been solved here in a very elementary way. It is, therefore, also impossible to check the solution, except by experiments. This has been done in another situation by Wierenga & de Wit (1970), who also considered the influence of temperature on the thermal conductivity of the soil, to account for heat transfer in the vapour phase. In general, common sense and the knowledge that in more simple situations correct answers are obtained must give confidence in the results.

# 3  Transport of a salt

## 3.1  Basic equations

Saline soils are often reclaimed by keeping a layer of fresh water on
top of the soil. In situations where water does not drain to deeper layers,
the salt is removed from the soil by diffusion to this fresh water. This
diffusion process is similar to the diffusion of heat into the soil and may
be simulated in principle with the heat flow program of Section 2.2, the
proper values for the diffusion characteristics of the main salt in the soil
and the proper initial conditions being substituted.

The diffusion coefficient (DIF) is expressed in $cm^2\,day^{-1}$ and the
concentration (CONC) in $mmol\,cm^{-3}$, so that, if the gradient is in
$mmol\,cm^{-3}\,cm^{-1}$, the rate of diffusion is in $mmol\,cm^{-2}\,day^{-1}$. The
diffusion coefficient in soil is less than in pure water for two reasons.
Firstly, only part of the soil volume is occupied by water and diffusion
is restricted to this part. Secondly, the water-filled pores in the soil are
not straight capillaries in the vertical direction, but form a labyrinth,
so that the diffusion length between two surfaces is longer than their
distance apart. To obtain the diffusion coefficient in the soil, the
coefficient in water must be multiplied by the water content (WC) and
the labyrinth factor (LAB). The water content is expressed in $cm^3$
water per $cm^3$ soil, and the labyrinth factor is dimensionless. This
labyrinth factor depends on the water content. So little is known about
this factor, that it is generally assumed to be a constant less than one.
The rise in temperature of a soil compartment is found by dividing the
net flow of heat by the thickness of the compartment and the specific
heat. Likewise the rise in concentration of the salt in a compartment is
found by dividing the net flow of salt by the thickness and the water
content of the compartment.

The flow by diffusion into compartment I, the geometry being given
in Fig. 11 is

$$DFFLOW(I) = \frac{CONC(I-1) - CONC(I)}{TCOM} * WC *$$

$$LAB * DIF \tag{3.1}$$

if the soil is uniform and divided into equal compartments with thickness $TCOM$. The concentration rise due to this flow into the compart-

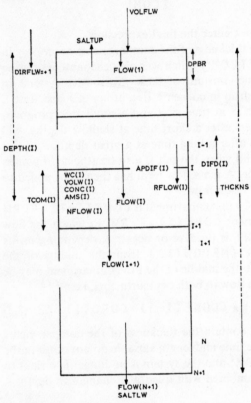

Fig. 11 | Geometry of the system and symbols, used in the program for the vertical transport of salt.

ment over the finite time interval DELT is

$$\Delta CON = \frac{DFFLOW}{TCOM*WC} * DELT = CONC(I-1) -$$

$$CONC(I) * LAB * DIF * \frac{DELT}{TCOM^2} \qquad (3.2)$$

The water content does not enter the final expression.

The time interval and the thickness of the compartments occur only in the combination DELT/TCOM², which was also encountered during the derivation of the time constant of these distributive systems in Section 2.3. Therefore a drop in concentration at depth $x$ and time $t$, will also occur at depth $n.x$ at time $n^2.t$ and a simulation program, which gives correct answers after a short time at shallow depths, will also give correct answers after a long time at a great depth.

This conclusion is not valid when the salt is also transported by mass flow of water in the profile. A mass flow term has then to be added to the expression for the diffusion flow.

The mass flow in the (I−1)th compartment is CONC(I−1)*FLRW and in the Ith compartment CONC(I)*FLRW, in which the flow rate of the water (FLRW) is positive or negative, depending on its direction. The mass flow (MFLOW(I)) from the middle of the (I−1)th compartment to the middle of the Ith compartment may be obtained by averaging the flow in both compartments, i.e.:

$$MFLOW(I) = FLRW*(CONC(I-1)+CONC(I))/2 \qquad (3.3)$$

This expression does not contain the thickness of the compartments as a parameter, so that the time and length variable do not occur in the combination DELT/TCOM² and the system is no longer invariant to linear changes in time, combined with quadratic changes in depth.

The effect of the water flow is not completely accounted for by the above equations, because the pores in the soil form a labyrinth with channels of various size and direction. The water moves fast in the wide channels and with it the salt in these channels and slowly in the narrow channels and more or less dead spaces. This disperses the salt in the direction of the movement of the water. The dispersion flow is proportional to the concentration gradient and the absolute flow rate of water:

```
DPFLOW(I) = DISP * |FLRW| *
CONC(I-1)-CONC(I)                           (3.4)
─────────────────
     TCOM
```

When the concentration gradient is expressed in mmol $cm^{-3}cm^{-1}$, the dispersion flow in mmol $cm^{-2}day^{-1}$ and the absolute flow rate of water in $cm\ day^{-1}$, then the dispersion factor (DISP) has the unit cm. According to Frissel et al. (1970), its value ranges from about 0.7 for coarse sand to 7 cm for löss. With a very small water flow of 1 cm $day^{-1}$ and a dispersion factor of 3 cm, the product of 3 $cm^2$ $day^{-1}$ is already 10 times larger than the product of diffusion coefficient, water content and labyrinth factor ($1 \times 0.5 \times 0.6$). Thus, under far the most conditions the influence of diffusion on the transport of ions is small compared with dispersion. The influence of both of them may be again small compared with the influence of mass flow of water.

The above approach seems straightforward, but the introduction of compartments of finite size to simulate the transport by mass flow may lead to serious errors. To show this error a saturated soil is considered with a sharp boundary between salt and fresh water. It is assumed that the diffusion coefficient of the salt and the dispersion coefficient of the soil are negligibly small and that the soil is infiltrated at a constant rate perpendicular to the sharp front. In this situation the boundary moves with a velocity equal to the infiltration rate divided by the water content and does not disperse during the movement. However, if this situation is simulated by means of compartments of finite size, considerable distortion of the concentration profile occurs, as is illustrated in Fig. 12. Glueckauf (1955) showed that this distortion is negligible when the thickness of the compartments is taken smaller then two times the dispersion factor plus the quotient of the apparent diffusion coefficient and the flow rate, i.e. when:

```
TCOM < 2*(DISP + WC*LAB*DIF/FLRW)
```

That this is indeed the case is shown in Figs 13 and 14 where analytical and simulated concentration profiles are compared in two limiting situations.

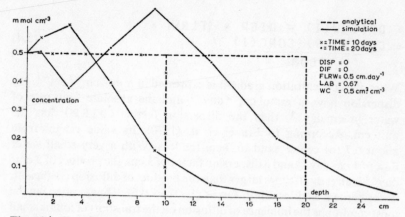

Fig. 12 | The distortion of the salt profile with a compartmentalized simulation program in situations where a sharp boundary persists.

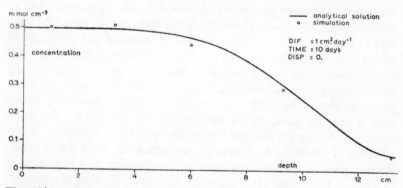

Fig. 13 | Analytical and simulated concentration profile in the absence of dispersion.

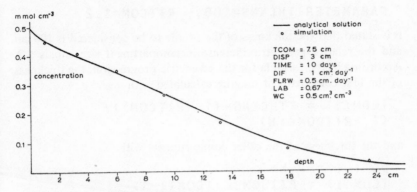

Fig. 14 | Analytical and simulated concentration profile in the presence of dispersion.

## 3.2 Simulation program for linear system

The simulation program for the diffusion of salt out of a profile is in principle the same as for the diffusion of heat. However, the possibility of a stationary flow of water has to be introduced and since this may be accompanied by a moisture gradient within the profile, it is also necessary to introduce a variable water content. Moreover, it is convenient to introduce a regular increase of compartment sizes and to define in the initial section the number of compartments and the total depth of the profile, rather than the thickness of the first compartment. The symbols used in the subsequent program are given in Fig. 11. The program starts again with the initial section:

```
INITIAL
NOSORT
```

The lines:

```
FIXED I, N, K
PARAMETER N=13
```

state that there are counters I and K, to be used in the 'DO-loops' and that the number of the compartments is 13.
With the line:

37

```
PARAMETER THCKNS=100., RITCOM=1.2
```

it is stated that the thickness of the profile to be considered is 100 cm
and the relative geometric increase in compartment size equals 1.2.
According to the formula for the geometric progression, the thickness
of the first compartment may be calculated with

```
TCOM(1) = (THCKNS*(1.-RITCOM))/
(1.-RITCOM**N)
```

and the thickness of the other compartments with

```
DO 1 I = 2,N
TCOM(I) = RITCOM * TCOM(I-1)
1 CONTINUE
```

The diffusion distance from the surface to the middle of the first
compartment is now

```
DIFD(1) = 0.5*TCOM(1)
```

and the depth of the first compartment

```
DEPTH(1) = DIFD(1)
```

The diffusion distances from the Ith to the $(I+1)$th compartment and
the depth of the I-th compartment are now given by

```
DO 2 I = 2,N
DIFD(I) = 0.5*(TCOM(I-1)+TCOM(I))
DEPTH(I) = DEPTH (I-1)+DIFD(I)
2 CONTINUE
```

The depth should be printed for further inspection with

```
WRITE(6,100) DEPTH
100 FORMAT (1Hb,5HDEPTH//(10F10.4))
```

The diffusion coefficient of NaCl in water is given with

```
PARAMETER DIF=1.
```

the units $cm^2 day^{-1}$, define both, the length and time scale of the
program.
The water content of the successive compartments is obtained with

```
FUNCTION WCTTB=(0.,0.5),(1000.,0.5)
DO 3 I = 1,N
WC(I) = AFGEN(WCTTB, DEPTH(I))
3 CONTINUE
```

The program is written in such a way that it can be used with only slight changes for the diffusion in a cylindrical or spherical system. Under these conditions, the surface area between the compartments should also be defined. In the present case of linear geometry, this is done with

```
K = N+1
DO 4 I = 1,K
AREA(I) = 1.
4 CONTINUE
```

there being one more boundary than compartments. The volume of water in each compartment is now calculated with

```
DO 5 I = 1,N
VOLW(I) = 0.5*(AREA(I)+AREA(I+1))*
TCOM(I)*WC(I)
5 CONTINUE
```

In cylindrical and spherical systems, the flow rate of water depends on the distance from the centre. It is therefore convenient not to define the rate of flow but the volume of flow in $cm^3$ per day (for cylinder and sphere), or $cm^3$ per day (per $cm^2$) for the linear case, with

```
PARAMETER VOLFLW = 3., DIRFLW = 1.
```

The flow is taken as positive in the downward direction. Now the flow rates over the boundaries are obtained with

```
DO 55 I = 1,K
RFLOW(I) = VOLFLW/AREA(I)
55 CONTINUE
```

which means for the linear case that the rate of flow equals the volume of flow as the area is 1 $cm^2$. For the cylindrical and the spherical system, the flow rate will decrease with increasing distance from the centre.

The apparent diffusion coefficient, divided by the diffusion distance is calculated for the boundary between two consecutive compartments with

```
DO 6 I = 1,N
```

The depth of each boundary is

```
DPBR = DEPTH(I)-0.5*TCOM(I)
```

and the product of water content and labyrinth factor at each boundary:

```
WCTLB = AFGEN(WCTTB,DPBR)*AFGEN(LABTB,
DPBR)
FUNCTION LABTB = (0.,0.67),(1000.,0.67)
```

and the product of dispersion factor and flow rate of the water at each boundary:

```
FUNCTION DISPTB = (0.,3.),(1000.,3.)
DSFW = AFGEN(DISPTB,DPBR)*RFLOW(I)
```

so that the apparent diffusion coefficient, divided by the diffusion distance equals

```
APDIF(I) = AREA(I)*(WCTLB*DIF+DSFW)/
DIFD(I)
6 CONTINUE
```

The more sophisticated way of averaging as used in the heat flow program (Section 2.2) could be used here to account for the difference in thickness of the compartments. However, this is not worth the trouble because the parameters do not change rapidly with depth and are anyhow not exactly known. For the flow of the first compartment to the surface, it is also of little importance whether the parameters are read at $0.5*DEPTH(1)$ or at the surface.

The amount of salt in each compartment is now initialised with

```
FUNCTION INTCNT = (0.,0.5),(1000.,0.5)
```

this being the concentration of sea water in mmol $cm^{-3}$, dependent on depth and with

```
DO 7 I = 1,N
IAMS(I) = VOLW(I)*AFGEN(INTCNT,
DEPTH(I))
7 CONTINUE
```

40

The program may be written more concisely, but this does not improve readability and it is not worth saving the computer time. Now we may proceed with the dynamic section:

```
DYNAMIC
NOSORT
```

The concentration of salt is calculated from the amount of salt in each compartment with

```
DO 8 I = 1,N
CONC(I) = AMS(I)/VOLW(I)
8 CONTINUE
```

and the concentration at the surface is

```
PARAMETER CONCS = 0.
```

The flow of salt from the surface into the first compartment is calculated with

```
FLOW(1) = APDIF(1)*(CONCS-CONC(1))+
VOLFLW*DIRFLW * (CONC(1) + CONCS)/2.
```

The flow over the other boundaries is

```
DO 9 I = 2,N
FLOW(I)=APDIF(I)*(CONC(I-1)-CONC(I))+
VOLFLW*DIRFLW*(CONC(I)+CONC(I-1))/2.
9 CONTINUE
```

whereas the flow out of or into the N-th compartment is

```
FLOW(N+1) = VOLFLW*DIRFLW*CONC(N)
```

It is supposed that concentration changes in this compartment are still negligible. The net flow into the compartments is

```
DO 10 I = 1,N
NFLW(I) = FLOW(I)-FLOW(I+1)
10 CONTINUE
```

The integration is again carried out with

```
AMS1 = INTGRL(IAMS1, NFLW1,30)
/ EQUIVALENCE(AMS1,AMS(1)),(IAMS1,
IAMS(1)),(NFLW1,NFLW(1))
/ REAL AMS(30),IAMS(30),NFLW(30)
```

It is impossible to substitute N for the number of integrals in this structural CSMP statement and to define N on a parameter card. Therefore, a sufficiently large number, 30, of integrals is generated to allow for a variable number of compartments.

The amounts of salt that pass the upper and lower boundary of the profile are

```
SALTUP=INTGRL(0.,FLOW(1))
SALTLW=INTGRL(0.,FLOW(N+1))
```

As before, all arrays which are not used in the integral function, have to be declared on STORAGE cards, the method of integration has to be defined, the timer specified and the output organised.

Table 1 gives the results of some runs with zero water flow.

*Table 1* The diffusion rate of salt in mmol cm$^{-2}$ day$^{-1}$ out of a profile with an initial salt concentration of 0.5 mmol cm$^{-3}$ as calculated from the analytical solution and as simulated for soil profiles with different thicknesses, without water flow.

|  | simulated | | | | analytical |
|---|---|---|---|---|---|
| THCKNS (cm) | 22 | 44 | 88 | 100 | |
| N | 13 | 13 | 13 | 13 | |
| RITCOM | 1.2 | 1.2 | 1.2 | 1.2 | |
| TCOM(1) (cm) | 0.5 | 1.0 | 2.0 | 8.75 | |
| DELT (days) | 0.2 | 0.4 | 0.769 | 3.57 | |
| | | | | | |
| TIME (days) | diffusion rates | | | | |
| 10 | 0.0365 | 0.0367 | 0.0379 | | 0.0366 |
| 40 | 0.0182 | 0.0182 | 0.0184 | | 0.0183 |
| 100 | 0.0115 | 0.0115 | 0.0116 | 0.0116 | 0.0115 |
| 200 | 0.0086 | 0.00815 | 0.00816 | 0.00816 | 0.00816 |
| 1000 | | | | 0.00364 | 0.00364 |

A comparison with the analytical solution shows that the simulation with thin layers and consequently a small time interval gives correct results after 10 days. Deviations occur after 200 days because by then the concentration in the last compartment is altered. On the other hand, the simulation with thick layers gives wrong results in the early stage, but correct results after 100 days. This was to be expected from the occurence of the time and depth parameter in the combination $DELT/TCOM^2$, only.

The simulated concentration profiles after 40 days with a downward water flow of 0. and 0.5 cm day$^{-1}$ are given in Fig. 15 and the total amounts of salt removed from the profile after 10, 20 and 40 days in Table 2. To avoid distortion, the thickness of the compartments was set equal to two times the dispersion length. As is to be expected, the salt is only removed from the profile by diffusion if the infiltration of water in the soil is negligible. If some infiltration occurs, no salt is removed by diffusion and all measures to improve infiltration have to be taken to remove any salt at all.

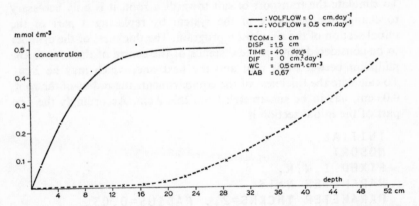

Fig. 15 | Simulated concentration profiles after 40 days with a downward waterflow of 0. and 0.5 cm day$^{-1}$.

*Table 2* Total amounts of salt in mmol cm$^{-2}$ removed from a profile of 100 cm with an initial concentration of 0.5 mmol cm$^{-3}$, with a downward flow of 0 and 0.5 cm day$^{-1}$. SALTUP through upper boundary, SALTLW through lower boundary.

| VELOCITY (cm day$^{-1}$) | SALTUP (mmol cm$^{-2}$) | | SALTLW (mmol cm$^{-2}$) | |
|---|---|---|---|---|
| | 0. | 0.5 | 0. | 0.5 |
| TIME (days): 10 | 0.6567 | 0.0468 | 0. | 2.50 |
| 20 | 0.9855 | 0.0505 | 0. | 4.99 |
| 40 | 1.4286 | 0.0518 | 0. | 9.37 |

## 3.3 Simulation program for cylindrical system

To simulate the transport of salt towards a root, it is only necessary to change the geometry of the system by replacing a part of the initial section of the simulation program. The thickness of the cylinder to be considered now, is the distance of the centre of the root to the midpoint between this root and the next one, which may be 2 cm. To calculate the thickness of the compartments the radius of the root, 0.03 cm, has to be substracted from this 2 cm. Accordingly the first part of the initial section is

```
INITIAL
NOSORT
FIXED I,N,K,
PARAMETER N=13
PARAMETER THCKNS=2., RADIUS=0.03,
RITCOM=1.2
```

and the thickness of the first compartment is obtained with

```
TCOM(1)= (THCKNS-RADIUS)*(1.-RITCOM)/
(1.-RITCOM**N))
```

The thickness of the compartments and their depths from the root surface and the diffusion distances between the compartments are calculated in the same way as in the linear case, as are the water

44

content and the labyrinth factor. The diffusion area between the compartments is then calculated with

```
K = N+1
DO 4 I = 2,K
AREA(I) = (DEPTH(I-1)+0.5*TCOM(I-1)+
RADIUS)*6.2832
4 CONTINUE
```

assuming that the compartments have a height of 1 cm.

Since the diffusion area within the first compartment changes rapidly with the radius, better results are obtained by supposing that the apparent diffusion coefficient from this compartment to the root depends on the area at half of the depth of this compartment, rather than on the area of the root, i.e.

```
AREA(1) = (0.25*TCOM(1)+RADIUS)*6.2832
```

These are all the changes that are necessary.

The profile of concentration that results after three hours of diffusion towards a root is shown in Fig. 16. The full line is the analytical solution and the points are simulated solutions, the cylinder of 2 cm being divided in 7, 13 or 24 compartments. It should be noted that the most coarse grid of only 7 compartments gives very acceptable solutions, even after only three hours of diffusion. By using coarse

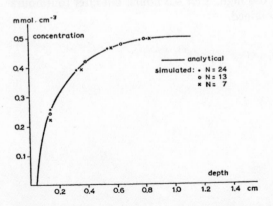

Fig. 16 | Analytical and simulated concentration profiles after 3 hours of diffusion towards a root.

45

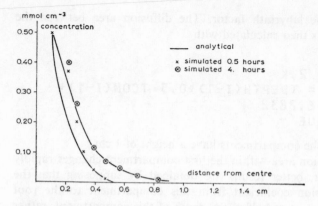

Fig. 17 | Analytical and simulated concentration profiles after 0.5 and 4 hours of diffusion from a sphere with a radius of 0.1 cm.

grids, much computer time is saved, which becomes important when many calculations per compartment have to be made, to account for the diffusion of a mixture of ions and exchange phenomena between soil and solution.

The writing of the initial section for spherical geometry should not present any difficulties. In Fig. 17 the simulated concentration in the compartment adjacent to a sphere with a radius of 0.1 cm that acts as a source, is still too high, after 0.5 hours, but after four hours correct solutions are obtained.

# 4 Diffusion of ions

## 4.1 Basic processes

In the previous sections the salt NaCl was treated as a molecule which diffuses as a unit, although it consists of $Na^+$ and $Cl^-$ and the diffusion coefficient of $Cl^-$ is 1.5 times larger than that of $Na^+$. This would favour the transport of $Cl^-$. However, if $Cl^-$ moves only a little bit ahead of $Na^+$, then a small separation of charges would occur so that the diffusion of $Cl^-$ is reduced and the diffusion of $Na^+$ is increased by electromotive forces, until both diffuse at the same rate. A small separation of charges builds up such large electromotive forces that the separation between $Cl^-$ and $Na^+$ is undetectable. Thus for all practical purposes, electroneutrality is fully maintained throughout the solution.

The situation is much more complicated when more than two ions are involved. For instance, the diffusion coefficient of $K^+$ is about the same as that for $Cl^-$, so that in a mixture of $Na^+$, $K^+$ and $Cl^-$, the diffusion coefficient of the $Cl^-$ is still reduced and that of the $Na^+$ increased and electroneutrality is maintained. However, the ions involved are now not necessarily diffusing at the same rate, so that the composition of the solution may change along the axis of diffusion. Under these conditions, the diffusion of each ion is governed by the gradient in concentration and the gradient in electromotive potential. As before, the flow under the influence of the gradient in concentration over a finite small distance DX is approximately:

$$FLOW = - DIF*DC/DX \qquad (4.1)$$

in which DC stands for the difference in concentration of the ion over the finite length DX and the negative sign indicates that the direction of flow is opposite to the direction in which the concentration increases. Likewise, the flow under influence of an electromotive potential difference DE in volts over a finite distance DX is approximately:

$$FLOW = \pm CONSTANT*DE/DX \qquad (4.2)$$

in which the minus sign holds for the negative ions which move against the potential gradient and the positive sign for the positive ions, which move with the potential gradient.

The flow under the influence of both the concentration and potential difference, is therefore:

$$FLOW = - DIF*DC/DX \pm CONSTANT*DE/DX \qquad (4.3)$$

The next problem is to express the unknown constant in this formula in known parameters. Firstly, the diffusion coefficient accounts for the frictional forces and since these forces are the same, whatever the driving forces are, this unknown constant is proportional to the diffusion coefficient. Secondly, the force on an ion due to a potential difference is proportional to the valency of the ion, i.e. two times larger for a divalent than for a mono-valent ion and of course the flow of ions in an electrical field is proportional to the concentration. To eliminate the troublesome $\pm$ sign before the constant, it is assumed that the valency (VAL) of positive ions is positive and of negative ions negative. Hence, the above Eqn (4.3) may be rewritten as follows:

$$FLOW = DIF*(-DC/DX+C*VAL*CNF*DE/DX) \qquad (4.4)$$

in which the conversion factor CNF has the unit $volt^{-1}$ (the electrical potential being expressed in volts) and is independent of the kind of ion and its concentration.

Hence for the flow of every ion (I) in a solution holds according to Eqn (4.4):

$$FLOW(I) = DIF(I)*(-DC(I)/$$
$$DX+VAL(I)*C(I)*CNF*DE/DX) \qquad (4.5)$$

The product of the conversion factor and the potential gradient, CNF*DE/DX is the same for every ion and may be calculated according to Vervelde (1955). For this it is taken into account that electroneutrality is maintained or that the net flow of charges is zero:

$$\sum_{1}^{N} VAL(I)*FLOW(I) = 0. \qquad (4.6)$$

By substituting Eqn (4.5) for all ions 1, 2, ..., N in Eqn (4.6) and solving, the following expression is obtained:

48

$$CNF*DE/DX = \frac{\sum\limits_{1}^{N} VAL(I)*DIF(I)*DC(I)/DX}{\sum\limits_{1}^{N} VAL^2(I)*DIF(I)*C(I)} \qquad (4.7)$$

Using this expression in Eqn (4.5), the flow of any ion may be calculated from the diffusion coefficients, the valencies and the concentrations of all ions concerned. The equations are thus sufficient to calculate the flow rates of all the ions between the compartments in a simulation program.

By working out Eqns (4.5) and (4.7) for a neutral salt, it can be shown that the average diffusion coefficient of a salt is

$$DIF = \frac{DIF(1)*DIF(2)}{DIF(1)+DIF(2)} * \frac{|VAL(1)|+|VAL(2)|}{|VAL(1)|*|VAL(2)|} \qquad (4.8)$$

Although the numerical value for the conversion factor is not needed to calculate the ionic transport, it can also be used to calculate the potential gradient or to simulate the influence of other potentials. This numerical value is 40 volts$^{-1}$ and may be obtained by considering the equilibrium situation, where the flow of an ion, as given by Eqn (4.4) is zero.

In this situation, the amount of work to move an ion against the potential difference is the same as the amount of work to move an ion against its concentration difference and this equality will provide us with a value for the conversion factor.

The amount of work to move a mole of ion against a potential difference $DE$ is given by:

$$WORK = VAL*F*DE \qquad \text{coulomb-volt} \qquad (4.9)$$

in which $F$ is the Faraday constant of 96500 coulomb, i.e. the amount of electricity in one mole of a mono-valent ion and in which the potential difference is expressed in volts.

To calculate the amount of work to move a mole of ion against a concentration difference, it should be recalled that in dilute solutions, ions behave according to the gas law:

49

$$P * V = R * T$$

in which P is the osmotic pressure due to the presence of the ion, V the volume of the solution, T the absolute temperature and R a universal constant. As one mole of gas at a temperature of 20 °C occupies 22.4 l at atmospheric pressure or a pressure of 1000 grams $cm^{-2}$, it is evident that for one mole:

$$R * T = 22400 \, g * cm = 2.24 \times 10^6 \, coulomb * volts$$

or equivalent to the amount of work to move 224 grams over 100 cm against the forces of gravity. This amount of work may also be expressed in electrical units, conversion factors for energy being known in physics.

If, at constant temperature, a mole of gas in a cylinder with piston surface, S, is compressed over a small distance D L, the amount of work which is done, equals $P * S * D L = P * D V$ in which P is its pressure and D V the small volume change.

According to the gas law:

$$(V + D V) * (P + D P) = R * T$$

or

$$V * P + D P * V + D V * P + D P * D V = R * T$$

in which D P is the pressure change that accompanies the volume change D V of one mole of gas. Since $V * P = R * T$ and $D P * D V$ is negligibly small, it follows that $V * D P = P * D V$ or that the product of the volume and the change in pressure, is the amount of work to move a small amount of gas at constant temperature into a constant volume. The concentration difference of an ion over a finite distance D X in solution is accompanied by a difference in osmotic pressure due to the ion. Therefore, the amount of work to move one mole of ion from one place to the other against this osmotic pressure difference equals:

$$WORK = V * D P = R * T * D P / P$$

and because the relative pressure difference D P / P equals the relative concentration difference D C / C

$$WORK = R * T * D C / C \tag{4.10}$$

The electrical and osmotic work being the same in the equilibrium situation, it follows from Eqns (4.9) and (4.10) that

50

$$VAL * F * DE = R * T * DC / C$$

or that

$$DC = VAL * C * (F / (R * T)) * DE$$

or that the conversion factor in Eqn (4.4) equals

$$CNF = F / (R * T) = 96500/2.24 \times 10^3 = 40 \text{ volt}^{-1} \tag{4.11}$$

at 20 °C, which number is needed to calculate the actual value of the potential difference.

## 4.2 Simulation program for linear system

Sufficient spade-work has been done now, to construct a simulation program for the diffusion of an arbitrary number of ions in a mixture. This will be done for a solution with 4 ions and a system with linear geometry in which 13 compartments are distinguished. However, the program will be written so, that with only slight changes it can be used for another number of ions and compartments.
It is supposed that the water content is constant and that any flow of water is absent. This assumption is made, not because the introduction of flow of water gives any difficulties, but because it is useless to introduce different diffusion coefficients for the individual ions when the diffusion coefficients are completely overruled by the dispersion coefficient under influence of water flow. It may even be, that the degree of refinement introduced in this section is wasted on a soil system. The problem is, however, treated because it is a good example of what may be done with simulation in physical chemistry and because it may be of use for the simulation in cases where root potentials are involved.
In the initial section, the parameters of the compartments are defined as before:

| | |
|---|---|
| TCOM(J) | thickness |
| DIFD(J) | diffusion distance |
| DEPTH(J) | depth |
| AREA(J) | area |
| N | number of compartments |

The water content and the labyrinth factor are supposed to be constant:

51

```
PARAMETER WC=0.4, LAB=0.67
```
With
```
PARAMETER K=4
```
the number of ions is defined.

The diffusion coefficient, the valency and the initial concentration of the 4 ions are defined on table cards:
```
TABLE DIF(1-4) = 0.6, 0.6, 1.2, 1.2
```
in $cm^2 day^{-1}$,
```
TABLE VAL(1-4) = +1, +2, -2, -1
TABLE INTCON(1-4) = 0.01, 0.005, 0.005,
0.01
```
in $mmol\ cm^{-3}$.

At this stage it should be checked carefully whether the sum of the product of the valency and the initial concentration is indeed zero, so that at least a possible situation is initialised.

The apparent diffusion coefficient for the K ions between the compartments and the volume of each compartment are defined by
```
DO 2 J = 1,N
DO 2 I = 1,K
APDIF(I,J)=AREA(J)*LAB*WC*DIF(I)/DIFD(J)
VOLL(J)=(AREA(J)+AREA(J+1))*TCOM(J)*0.5
2 CONTINUE
```

in which the first index of APDIF indicates the ionic species and the second index the boundary, according to the convention of Fig. 18. This nested DO-loop sets first the number J for the compartments at 1, then gives then the diffusion coefficients for the K ions in this compartment, and then repeats the process for compartment 2 to compartment N.

The volume of water in each compartment is calculated with
```
DO 3 J = 1,N
VOLW(J) = 0.5*(AREA(J)+AREA(J+1))*
TCOM(J)*WC
3 CONTINUE
```

and the initial amount of ions in each compartment with

```
DO 4 J = 1,N
DO 4 I = 1,K
IAION(I,J) = VOLW(J)*INTCON(I)
4 CONTINUE
```

The

```
TABLE CONS(1-4) = 4*0.
```

states that the concentration of the 4 ions at the surface is zero.
The dynamic section of the program will be given in full.

```
DYNAMIC
NOSORT
```

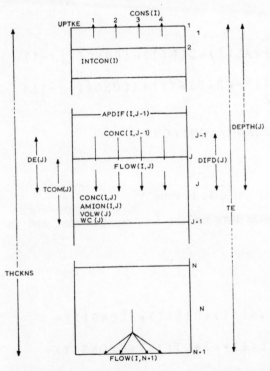

Fig. 18 | Geometry of the system and symbols, used in the program for the transport of ions.

The concentration of the 4 ions in the 13 compartments is calculated from the amount of ions in the compartments with

```
DO 5 J = 1,N
DO 5 I = 1,K
CONC(I,J) = AMION(I,J)/VOLW(J)
5 CONTINUE
```

The potential difference (DE) between the compartments is obtained according to Eqn (4.7) by the following DO-loop:

```
DO 6 J = 2,N
```

The value of the denominator and nominator of the expression is first calculated:

```
DENOM = 0.
NOM = 0.
DO 7 I = 1,K
DENOM=DENOM+VAL(I)*DIF(I)*(CONC(I,J-1)-
CONC(I,J))
NOM=NOM+VAL(I)**2*DIF(I)*(CONC(I,J-1)+
CONC(I,J))/2
7 CONTINUE
DE(J) = - (DENOM/NOM)/CNF
6 CONTINUE
```

with

```
PARAMETER CNF = 40. in volts⁻¹
```

The potential difference between the first compartment and the surface is

```
DENOM = 0.
NOM = 0.
DO 8 I = 1,K

DENOM=DENOM+VAL(I)*DIF(I)*(CONS(I)-
CONC(I,1))
NOM = NOM+VAL(I)**2*DIF(I)*(CONS(I)+
CONC(I,1))/2
8 CONTINUE
DE(1) = -(DENOM/NOM)/CNF
```

54

As in the previous program, a flow downward is represented by a positive sign. This means that here a negative sign has to be added to the calculation of DE. Errors with signs are easily made, but also easily detected in the first run of the program.

The flow of ions from the surface to the first compartment is

```
DO 9 I = 1,K
DCONC = CONS(I) - CONC(I,1)
ACONC = 0.5*(CONS(I)+CONC(I,1))
FLOW(I,1) = APDIF(I,1)*(DCONC+VAL(I)*
ACONC*CNF*DE(1))
```

whereas the flow out of the 13th compartment is

```
FLOW(I,14) = 0.
9 CONTINUE
```

The flow from one compartment to the next is calculated with

```
DO 10 J = 2,N
DO 10 I = 1,K
DCONC = CONC(I,J-1)-CONC(I,J)
ACONC = 0.5*(CONC(I,J-1)+CONC(I,J))
FLOW(I,J) = APDIF(I,J)*(DCONC+VAL(I)*
ACONC*CNF*DE(J))
10 CONTINUE
```

The net flow of the 4 ions into the 13 compartments is

```
DO 11 J = 1,N
DO 11 I = 1,K
NFLW(I,J) = FLOW(I,J)-FLOW(I,J+1)
11 CONTINUE
```

and the amount of each ion in each compartment is given by

```
AMION1 = INTGRL(IAION1, NFLW1,52)
/ EQUIVALENCE (AMION1, AMION(1,1)),
(IAION1, IAION(1,1)), (NFLW1, NFLW(1,1))
/ REAL IAION(4,13), NFLW(4,13),
AMION(4,13)
```

Because electro-neutrality is maintained, the amount of one ionic

55

species can be calculated from the other three. Hence it is only necessary to calculate the integrals of 3 species instead of 4. This saves about 25% computing time. The program is not written in this way to improve readability. It is a good exercise to rewrite the program for $3 \times 13$ integrals.

All arrays, which are used in tables may be 'declared' with a STORAGE statement:

```
STORAGE DIF(4), VAL(4), INTCON(4),
CONS(4)
```

and the other arrays with

```
/ REAL FLOW(4,14), TCOM(13), DIFD(13),
APDIF(4,13), DEPTH(13), AREA(14),
VOLL(13)
/ REAL VOLW(13), CONC(4,13), DE(13)
```

The dynamic section of the simulation is finished with

```
METHOD MILNE
```

and

```
TIMER FINTIM=100., OUTDEL=10., PRDEL=1.
```

in which OUTDEL is used to control the output of the arrays, as will be shown, and PRDEL to control the output of the CSMP print routine.

The output can be specified again, using the print and plot routines of CSMP. However, so many arrays have to be 'undimensionalized' for this, that it is more convenient to use FORTRAN output capabilities. For this purpose the program continues with

```
WRT = IMPULS(0.,OUTDEL)
IF(WRT*KEEP.LT.0.5)GO TO 12
WRITE (6,100) TIME
WRITE (6,101) CONC(1,J)
WRITE (6,102) CONC(2,J)
WRITE (6,103) CONC(3,J)
WRITE (6,104) CONC(4,J)
WRITE (6,105) DE(J)
12 CONTINUE
```

WRT is zero except when the IMPULS function sets it to 1 at times

56

$0,0+OUTDEL,0+2*OUTDEL$ and so on. The internal CSMP variable 'KEEP' is 1 when the actual rates of change of the integrals are calculated and is zero when intermediate rates, necessary for more sophisticated integration techniques are calculated (see Section 1.3). Hence the statement 'IF WRT*KEEP' IS LESS THAN 0.5, then GO TO 12, transfers the calculation to the continue card with this statement number, except when output is needed. Only when and WRT and KEEP are equal to 1, are the WRITE statements carried out. The six WRITE statements request to print: the time, the concentration of the first ion in all 13 compartments, then of the second, third and fourth ion and then of the difference in electro-chemical potential between the surface and the first compartment and between the successive compartments. The layout and the text above the rows with numbers are given on the FORMAT statements, numbered 100–105:

```
100 FORMAT (1Hb,4HTIME//F16.8)
101 FORMAT (1Hb,37HCONC MONOV CATION AT
DIFFERENT DEPTHS//13F10.4)
102 FORMAT (1Hb,35HCONC DIV CATION AT
DIFFERENT DEPTHS//13F10.4)
103 FORMAT (1Hb,39HCONC DIV ANION AT
DIFFERENT DEPTHS//13F10.4)
104 FORMAT (1Hb,36HCONC MONOV ANION AT
DIFFERENT DEPTHS//13F10.4)
105 FORMAT (1Hb,36HPOT GRADIENT BETWEEN
SUCCESSIVE COMP//13F10.4)
```

Just as in FORTRAN, the output has to be organised carefully. One may also be interested in the total potential drop over the compartments (TE) and the total amount of ions taken up by the water (UPTKE1, and so on). These are calculated with

```
TE = 0.
DO 13 J = 1,N
TE = TE+DE(J)
13 CONTINUE
UPTKE1 = INTGRL(0.,-FLOW(1,1))
UPTKE2 = INTGRL(0.,-FLOW(2,1))
UPTKE3 = INTGRL(0.,-FLOW(3,1))
UPTKE4 = INTGRL(0.,-FLOW(4,1))
```

```
DIFFUSION OF IONS, LINEAR CASE,                                   MILNE     INTEGRATION
  TIME         UPTKE1       UPTKE2       UPTKE3       UPTKE4      TE          TELLER.      DELT
1.1000E 02   1.0152E 00   1.0940E 00   1.1794E 00   1.0119E 00  -2.1578E-02  1.6200E 02   2.0000E 00
1.1200E 02   1.0246E 00   1.1041E 00   1.1902E 00   1.0212E 00  -2.1622E-02  1.6400E 02   2.0000E 00
1.1400E 02   1.0338E 00   1.1140E 00   1.2009E 00   1.0305E 00  -2.1666E-02  1.6600E 02   2.0000E 00
1.1600E 02   1.0430E 00   1.1239E 00   1.2116E 00   1.0396E 00  -2.1708E-02  1.6800E 02   2.0000E 00
1.1800E 02   1.0521E 00   1.1337E 00   1.2221E 00   1.0487E 00  -2.1750E-02  1.7000E 02   2.0000E 00
TIME

  120.00000000
CONC MONOV CATION AT DIFFERENT DEPTHS

  0.0212    0.0666    0.1165    0.1658    0.2067    0.2333    0.2455    0.2492    0.2499    0.2500    0.2500    0.2500    0.2500
CONC DIV CATION AT DIFFERENT DEPTHS

  0.0195    0.0616    0.1086    0.1563    0.1985    0.2283    0.2436    0.2488    0.2498    0.2500    0.2500    0.2500    0.2500
CONC DIV ANION AT DIFFERENT DEPTHS

  0.0183    0.0579    0.1023    0.1483    0.1902    0.2218    0.2400    0.2475    0.2496    0.2499    0.2500    0.2500    0.2500
CONC MONOV ANION AT DIFFERENT DEPTHS

  0.0209    0.0660    0.1157    0.1651    0.2068    0.2340    0.2463    0.2496    0.2500    0.2500    0.2500    0.2500    0.2500
POT GRADIENT BETWEEN SUCCESSIVE.COMP

 -0.0099   -0.0051   -0.0027   -0.0018   -0.0012   -0.0007   -0.0003   -0.0001   -0.0000   -0.0000   -0.0000   -0.0000   -0.0000
```

Fig. 19 | Example of the output of the program for the transport of ions, generated with the WRITE and PRINT capability.

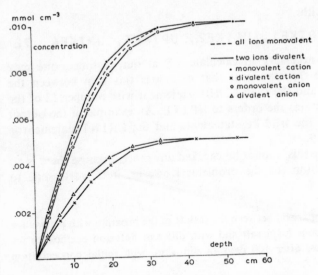

Fig. 20a | Simulated concentration profiles for different valencies of the ions after 200 days of diffusion in a 4 ionic system.

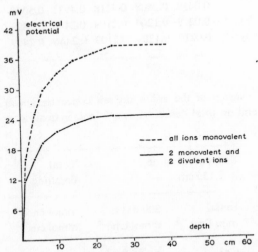

Fig. 20b | Simulated potential profiles for different valencies of the ions after 200 days of diffusion in a 4 ionic system.

and printed with:

```
PRINT UPTKE1, UPTKE2, UPTKE3, UPTKE4, TE
```

As it is only necessary to calculate TE at output times, one may want to place the statement that calculates this sum between the IF-statement and the CONTINUE-statement with number 12 of the block that contains the orders to WRITE. An example of the output obtained with the WRITE-statements and the PRINT-statement is given in Fig. 19.

A program like this, cannot be checked any more, because there is no analytical solution for the problem. However, it is worthwhile to

*Table 3*  A comparison between the results of the program with an average diffusion coefficient for a salt and with different diffusion coefficients for the 2 ion species, after 100 days of diffusion, with initial concentration of 0.5 mmol cm$^{-3}$.

| | concentration in mmol cm$^{-3}$ at: | | | | |
|---|---|---|---|---|---|
| | 1.1 | 6.6 | 14.5 | 25.9 | 53.0 cm |
| salt, $D = 0.8$ cm$^2$ day$^{-1}$ | 0.0439 | 0.2408 | 0.4218 | 0.4931 | 0.5000 |
| four ions: $D_{neg} = 1.2$ cm$^2$ day$^{-1}$ | 0.0219 | 0.1204 | 0.2109 | 0.2466 | 0.2499 |
| $D_{pos} = 0.6$ cm$^2$ day$^{-1}$ | 0.0219 | 0.1204 | 0.2109 | 0.2466 | 0.2499 |

*Table 4*  Influence of the valency of the anion on salt concentration at 1.135 cm from the surface and on total desalting, in a 2 ionic system, after 200 days.

| Pos. ion | | Neg. ion | | Saltconcentration at 1.135 cm | | Total desalting |
|---|---|---|---|---|---|---|
| Diff. coeff. cm$^2$ day$^{-1}$ | Val. | Diff. coeff. cm$^2$ day$^{-1}$ | Val. | Initial mmol cm$^{-3}$ | 200 days mmol cm$^{-3}$ | mmol cm$^{-2}$ mmol cm$^{-2}$ |
| 0.6 | +1 | 1.2 | −1 | 0.01 | $5.9454 \times 10^{-4}$ | $3.6179 \times 10^{-2}$ |
| 0.6 | +1 | 1.2 | −2 | 0.01 | $6.8706 \times 10^{-4}$ | $3.1288 \times 10^{-2}$ |

*Table 5* Influence of the valency of the ions on ionic concentration, total desalting and potential drop in a 4 ionic system, after 200 days.

| | pos. ion 1 | pos. ion 2 | neg. ion 1 | neg. ion 2 |
|---|---|---|---|---|
| valency | $+1$ | $+1$ | $-1$ | $-1$ |
| initial conc. ($mmol\ cm^{-3}$) | 0.01 | 0.01 | 0.01 | 0.01 |
| diff. coeff. ($cm^2\ day^{-1}$) | 0.6 | 0.6 | 1.2 | 1.2 |
| Ionic concentration at 1.135 cm ($mmol\ cm^{-3}$) | $5.945 \times 10^{-4}$ | $5.945 \times 10^{-4}$ | $5.945 \times 10^{-4}$ | $5.945 \times 10^{-4}$ |
| desalting ($mmol\ cm^{-2}$): 0.1447 | | | | |
| potential drop (volt): $-3.9169 \times 10^{-2}$ | | | | |
| | | | | |
| valency | $+1$ | $+2$ | $-1$ | $-2$ |
| initial conc. ($mmol\ cm^{-3}$) | 0.01 | 0.005 | 0.01 | 0.005 |
| diff. coeff. ($cm^2\ day^{-1}$) | 0.6 | 0.6 | 1.2 | 1.2 |
| ionic concentration at 1.135 cm ($mmol\ cm^{-3}$) | $6.483 \times 10^{-4}$ | $2.971 \times 10^{-4}$ | $5.740 \times 10^{-4}$ | $3.342 \times 10^{-4}$ |
| desalting ($mmol\ cm^{-2}$): 0.1742 | | | | |
| potential drop (volt): $-2.5502 \times 10^{-2}$ | | | | |

compare the outputs in two situations. One output from this program with the valency and the diffusion coefficient of 2 ions at $-1$ and $1.2\ cm^2 day^{-1}$ and of the other 2 ions at $+1$ and $0.6\ cm^2 day^{-1}$. The other output from the previous program (Section 3) for the diffusion of salt with an average diffusion coefficient of $0.8\ cm^2 day^{-1}$, calculated according to Eqn (4.8).
As shown in Table 3, the outcome is the same, so that at least the

present program does not contain conceptunal or programming errors. To show the influence of ionic composition on desalting and concentration, some results are summarized in tables 4 and 5 and Fig. 20. Table 4 shows that the concentration close to the surface after 200 days is higher and the total desalting lower, when the negative ion is divalent instead of monovalent and has a diffusion coefficient twice as high. Table 5 shows the concentration, total desalting and total potential drop for a 4 ion mixture in which the 2 positive ions have a diffusion coefficient of $0.6$ $cm^2 day^{-1}$ and the 2 negative ions of $1.2$ $cm^2 day^{-1}$, assuming that either all ions are monovalent or that one of the negative and one of the positive ions is divalent. For the latter situation the concentration of all the ions in both cases and the potential drop after 200 days are given in Fig. 20 as a function of the depth.

All the above situations refer to systems with linear geometry. In the same way as in the salt diffusion program, the program may be adapted to other geometrical systems by changing the statements that define the geometry. These statements are all found in the initial section.

# 5 Transport of ions in soil

## 5.1 Basic processes

In the previous chapter, the transport of ions was considered, under conditions where only a negligible fraction of the anions is immobile. This situation occurs in soils which consist of pure sand and may occur in other soils under saline conditions. However in many soils, the fraction of negative ions that is mobile in the solution is small compared with the immobile fraction. For instance, if the high amount of fertilizer of 400 kg ha$^{-1}$ of potassium nitrate is mixed in the first 10 centimeters of a soil with a moisture content of 0.5 cm$^3$ cm$^{-3}$, then the concentration of $NO_3^-$ equals 8 meq $NO_3^-$ liter$^{-1}$. However, if the soil has 30% clay, it may contain 200 meq immobile negative ions per liter soil, which amounts to 400 meq per liter water, a value which is still 50 times larger than the already high $NO_3^-$ content of the fertilized soil.

Because electroneutrality is maintained throughout, positive ions are associated with these negative ions in the matrix, but these may exchange with other positive ions in the soil solution. This exchange is a very rapid process, so that it is in general assumed that there is at any time an equilibrium between the concentrations of the positive ions in solution and on the soil matrix.

Although exchange processes in the soil are of great complexity, it may be supposed in a first approximation that the equilibrium between adsorbed ions and ions in solution is governed by the 'Law of Mass Action'. For a mixture of two ions I1 and I2 of the same valency, this means that the ratio of the ionic species in solution is proportional to the ratio of the species on the adsorption sites:

$$I1A/I2A = K*(I1S/I2S) \tag{5.1}$$

in which K is a dimensionless equilibrium constant and A and S indicate the ions associated with the adsorption complex and the solution, respectively. During the exchange, the total amount of positive ions in solution and on the adsorption complex and the total amounts of each ionic species do not change i.e.

$$I1A + I2A = TIA \quad \text{(total ions adsorbed)}$$
$$I1S + I2S = TIS \quad \text{(total ions in solution)}$$
$$I1A + I1S = TI1 \quad \text{(total ions of species 1)}$$
$$I2A + I2S = TI2 \quad \text{(total ions of species 2)}$$

These equations are used to eliminate $I2A$, $I1S$ and $I2S$ from the Mass Action Equation, which gives

$$(1-K) I1A^2 + (K*TIA + (K-1) TI1 + TIS) I1A - K*TIA*TI1 = 0 \tag{5.2}$$

and expresses the amount of adsorbed ionic species 1 in the total amounts of immobile and mobile ions involved. When all amounts of ions are expressed in equivalents per unit volume water in the soil, the equilibrium constant $K$ is dimensionless and varies for most combinations of ions of the same valency between 0.5 and 2. The exchange capacity ($EXCAP$) of a soil is usually given in milli-equivalents per gram of soil. If the specific weight of the soil is $SW$ and the water content $WC$, then the total amount of ions adsorbed equals:

$$TIA = EXCAP*SW/WC \text{ in meq cm}^{-3} \text{ of water.}$$

The same equations hold for systems that contain two divalent positive ions.

Since exchange occurs at a faster rate, compared with the rates of diffusion, dispersion and water flow, Eqn (5.2) may be used to calculate for any compartment at any time how much of each ionic species is in solution and adsorbed.

The Law of Mass Action in a mixture of one divalent and one mono-valent ion is more complicated than in mixtures of ions of the same valency. If the amount of ions adsorbed and in solution are both expressed per volume of water, i.e. meq liter$^{-1}$, the equilibrium constant $K$ in

$$DIS/DIA = K*(MIS/MIA)^2 \tag{5.3}$$

is dimensionless, but its value is proportional to the exchange capacity of the soil. The proportionality factor between $K$ and exchange capacity for the ions $K^+$ and $Ca^{2+}$ in equilibrium with clay is about 40 cm$^3$ soil meq$^{-1}$ if the exchange capacity is expressed in meq cm$^{-3}$

soil. The conservation equations are

$$DIA + MIA = TIA \quad \text{(total ions adsorbed)}$$
$$DIS + MIS = TIS \quad \text{(total ions in solution)} \tag{5.4}$$
$$MIA + MIS = TMI \quad \text{(total monovalent ions)}$$
$$DIA + DIS = TDI \quad \text{(total divalent ions)}$$

These equations again enable the concentration of one ionic species in solution to be expressed in the total concentrations and the equilibrium constant. However, as it is impossible to combine the relations to obtain an explicit expression a method of successive better approximations has to be adopted.

For this purpose an 'implicit function' is available in CSMP. This function directs the system to iterate according to a standard procedure, for which the user can specify the error criterion. For the present purpose, the function may be used as follows:

```
DIS=IMPL(GDIS,ERROR,FDIS)
MIS=TIS-DIS
MIA=TMI-MIS
DIA=TIA-MIA
FDIS=K*(MIS/MIA)²*DIA
```

The first line states that the series of statements ending with FDIS=--- is part of an implicit loop, which has to be solved. The first guess for the answer is GDIS and the iteration proceeds until the relative difference of two successive estimates satisfies the relative error, given in the argument of the first line. This relative error may be set at 0.01 and the first guess in a simulation program is usually the answer obtained in the previous time interval.

When the relative error criterion is not met after 100 iterations, CSMP halts the simulation. Experience has shown that this may occur with exchange problems, so that a special iterative procedure has been developed. This procedure is called upon by the sentence:

```
DIS = ADFUNC(TDI,TMI,TIA,K,GUESS)
```

in which DIS is the amount of divalent ions in solution that has to be calculated, TDI, TMI are the total amount of divalent and monovalent ions, K is the equilibrium constant and GUESS is a guessed value for DIS. The actual iteration procedure is given in Section 5.3.

## 5.2 Simulation program

A simulation program will now be given for the situation when the exchange capacity of the soil is not negligible and the soil solution contains one monovalent and one divalent positive ion and one negative ion. The linear case, with fresh water on the surface, is again considered and it is assumed that water flow may take place. Under these conditions the diffusion is small compared with dispersion, so that it is unrealistic to bother about small differences in diffusion coefficients between the ions and moreover the exchange equations are also approximations. The diffusion coefficients of the ions in the adsorbed phase are considered negligible, although there are indications, that this is not actually the case, especially for monovalent ions (Frère & de Wit, 1971). To avoid unnecessary repetition of more complicated constructions here, it is assumed that the labyrinth factor and the water content of the soil are constant throughout.

The parameters of the compartments:

| | |
|---|---|
| TCOM(J) | thickness compartments |
| DIFD(J) | diffusion distance |
| DEPTH(J) | depth |
| AREA(J) | area |
| VOLW(J) | volume of water |

are calculated as in Section 4.2.

The water content, the labyrinth factor, the dispersion factor in cm, the exchange capacity in meq cm$^{-3}$ of soil, the flow of water in cm$^3$ day$^{-1}$ (per cm$^2$), the direction of flow (+ downwards), the diffusion coefficient in cm$^2$ day$^{-1}$ and the number of compartments are

```
PARAMETER WC=0.4, LAB=0.67, DISP=3.,
EXCAP=0.2, FLWVOL=3., DIRFLW=+1.,
DIF=1., N=13
```

As the differences in diffusion coefficients are neglected, it is unnecessary to keep a separate track of the diffusion of the negative ion. Its concentration can be found at any time by adding together the concentrations of the positive ions in solution. It is assumed that ion 1 is monovalent and ion 2 divalent. Their initial concentrations are

```
TABLE INTCON(1-2)=2.,8.
```
meq cm$^{-3}$ water

The flow rate of water over the boundaries is

```
DO 1 J = 1,N
FLRW(J) = FLWVOL/AREA(J)
1 CONTINUE
```

Since it is assumed that the soil properties are constant throughout, the apparent diffusion coefficient may be simply calculated with

```
DO 2 J = 1,N
APDIF(J)=AREA(J)*(LAB*WC*DIF+FLRW(J)*
DISP)
2 CONTINUE
```

The concentration of the adsorbed ions in every compartment is

```
TIA=EXCAP/WC
```

and the dimensionless value of K is

```
K=CNK*EXCAP
PARAMETER CNK = 40.
```

in which the value of $40 \, cm^3$ of soil per meq holds for the ions $K^+$ and $Ca^{2+}$, in equilibrium with clay.
The concentration of the divalent ion on the adsorption complex is calculated now. Although this can be done with an explicit formula, readability is improved by using the implicit function. The first guess is

```
GDIA = 0.5*TIA
```

The error criterion is

```
PARAMETER ERROR = 0.01
```

and the answer is obtained with (Eqns 5.3 and 5.4)

```
DIA=IMPL(GDIA,ERROR,FDIA)
MIA=TIA-DIA
MIS=INTCON(1)
DIS=INTCON(2)
FDIA=DIS*(MIA/MIS)**2/K
MIA=TIA-DIA
```

The initial total amount of both ions in each compartment in meq is

```
DO 3 J = 1,N
IAMIN(1,J)=VOLW(J)*(INTCON(1)+MIA)
IAMIN(2,J)=VOLW(J)*(INTCON(2)+DIA)
3 CONTINUE
```

In the dynamic section an iteration has to be made. The first guess at time zero for the amount of divalent ions in solution for all compartments is

```
DO 4 J = 1,N
GDIS(J)=INTCON(2)
4 CONTINUE
```

The dynamic section will be given again in full.

```
DYNAMIC
NOSORT
```

For each compartment, the concentration of each ion in solution has to be calculated. This is done in a DO-loop that contains the iterative procedure

```
DO 5 J = 1,N
```

First the total concentrations of the monovalent and divalent ion are calculated with

```
TMI=AMION(1,J)/VOLW(J)
TDI=AMION(2,J)/VOLW(J)
```

Then the concentration of the divalent ion in solution is obtained with the iterative procedure:

```
GUESS = GDIS(J)
DIS = ADFUNC(TDI,TMI,TIA,K,GUESS)
```

The concentrations of the ions in solution are stored in arrays:

```
CONC(1,J) = DIS
MIS=TMI-TIA+TDI-DIS
CONC(2,J)=MIS
```

The first guess for the next time step is

```
GDIS(J)=DIS
5 CONTINUE
```

The concentration of both ions at the surface is again set to zero:

```
TABLE CONS(1-2)=2*0.
```

The flow from the surface into the first compartment is now calculated with

```
DO 6 I = 1,2
FLOW(I,1)=APDIF(1)*(CONS(I)-CONC(I,1))/
DIFD(1)+FLWVOL*DIRFLW*(CONS(I)+
CONC(I,1))/2
```

and out of the thirteenth compartment with

```
FLOW(I,14)=FLWVOL*DIRFLW*CONC(I,N)
```

it being supposed that concentration changes at that depth are still negligible.

```
6 CONTINUE
```

The flow over the other boundaries is

```
DO 7 J = 2,N
DO 7 I = 1,2
FLOW(I,J)=APDIF(J)*(CONC(I,J-1)-
CONC(I,J))/DIFD(J)+FLWVOL*DIRFLW*
(CONC(I,J-1) + CONC(I,J))/2
7 CONTINUE
```

The net flow of each ion into each of the compartments is

```
DO 8 J = 1,N
DO 8 I = 1,2
NFLOW(I,J)=FLOW(I,J)-FLOW(I,J+1)
8 CONTINUE
```

The amount of ions in each compartment is given by the CSMP statement:

```
AMION1=INTGRL(IAMIN1,NFLOW1,26)
/ EQUIVALENCE (AMION1,AMION(1,1)),
(IAMIN1,IAMIN(1,1)),(NFLOW1,NFLOW(1,1))
```

The program is finished like any of the other programs.

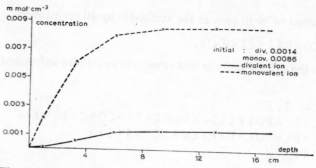

Fig. 21 | Concentration profiles of ions in solution after 10 days of diffusion out of the soil.

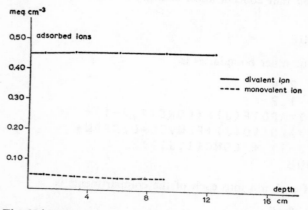

Fig. 22 | Concentration profiles of ions at the adsorption complex after 10 days of diffusion out of the soil.

As an example, the relation between the ionic concentrations and depth, 10 days after the initialisation of an experiment is shown in Fig. 21 and 22. It should be stressed here that the calculations are done for a uniform soil profile, but that the program can be easily changed to simulate non-uniform profiles, as has been shown before. The program can also be extended easily to more than two ions because the iterative procedure can be done for the pooled amounts of monovalent and divalent ions (Heald et al., 1964).

## 5.3 Iterative procedure

The iterative procedure that has been adopted is most conveniently explained graphically. The equations that have to be solved are

$$DIA = TDI-GDIS$$
$$MIA = TIA-DIA$$
$$MIS = TMI-MIA$$
$$DIS = K*(MIS/MIA)**2*DIA$$

in which DIS is the concentration of divalent ions in solution, GDIS an estimate of this value and the other symbols are the other concentrations involved, as defined in Section 5.1.

The correct solution is obtained if the calculated value of DIS minus GDIS is smaller than a limit of error which may be set at 0.005. This difference (FGS) is presented in Fig. 23 as a function of GDIS. Inspection of the

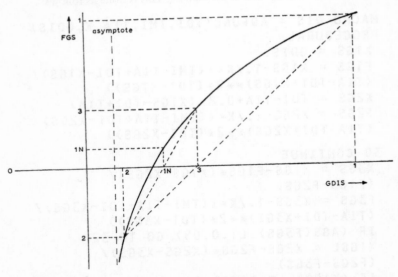

Fig. 23 | Graphic representation of the iterative procedure to calculate the amount of adsorbed ions.

four equations shows that $FGS$ is infinite for $MIA=0$ or for $GDIS=TDI-TIA$. This asymptotic value is presented in the graph. The proper value of $DIS$ is found at the intersection of the curve and the horizontal axis. For the first guess, $GDIS1$, the amount of divalent ions in solution at the previous time step is taken and a second guess, $GDIS2$, is obtained by taking a fraction of the difference between $GDIS1$ and the asymptote. With these two guesses, $FGS1$ and $FGS2$ are calculated, respectively. Subsequently, a third guess, $GDIS3$, is obtained by interpolation between the points $(GDIS1, FGS1)$ and $(GDIS2, FGS2)$. The last step is repeated to find a new guess, $GDIS1N$, between $GDIS2$ and $GDIS3$, and this continues until the function value $FGS$ is smaller than the limit of error. The corresponding value of $GDIS$ is then the value of $DIS$ which is wanted.

This procedure gives the correct answer within a few iterations under any circumstance.

In $CSMP$ the procedure is most conveniently introduced as a ′MACRO′, the use of which is described in the manual. This is done as follows:

```
MACRO DIS = ADFUNC(TDI,TMI,TIA,K,GDIS)
PROCEDURAL
 X1GS = GDIS
 F1GS = X1GS-1./K*((TMI-TIA+TDI-X1GS)/
 (TIA-TDI+X1GS)**2*(TDI-X1GS))
 X2GS = TDI-TIA+0.8*(X1GS-TDI+TIA)
 F2GS = X2GS-1./K*((TMI-TIA+TDI-X2GS)/
 (TIA-TDI+X2GS)**2*(TDI-X2GS))

30 CONTINUE
 X3GS = X1GS-F1GS*(X1GS-X2GS)/
 (F1GS-F2GS)
 F3GS = X3GS-1./K*((TMI-TIA+TDI-X3GS)/
 (TIA-TDI+X3GS)**2*(TDI-X3GS))
 IF (ABS(F3GS).LT.0.05) GO TO 32
 X1GSL = X2GS-F2GS*(X2GS-X3GS)/
 (F2GS-F3GS)
 IF (X1GSL.LT.X1GS) GO TO 33
 X1GS = X1GSL
 F1GS = X1GS-1./K*((TMI-TIA+TDI-X1GS)/
 (TIA-TDI+X1GS)**2*(TDI-X1GS))
 IF (ABS(F1GS).LT.0.05) GO TO 35
```

```
33 CONTINUE
   X2GSL = X1GS-F1GS*(X1GS-X3GS)/
   (F1GS-F3GS)
   IF (X2GSL.LT.X2GS) GO TO 30
   X2GS = X2GSL
   F2GS = X2GS-1./K*((TMI-TIA+TDI-X2GS)/
   (TIA-TDI+X2GS)**2*(TDI-X2GS))
   IF (ABS(F2GS).GT.0.05) GO TO 30
   DIS = X2GS
   GO TO 36

32 CONTINUE
   DIS = X3GS
   GO TO 36

35 CONTINUE
   DIS = X1GS

36 CONTINUE
ENDMAC
```

# 6 Infiltration of water in the soil

## 6.1 Basic problems

It is generally assumed that the driving forces of the water flow in the soil are fully compensated by frictional forces, so that the flow of water in a horizontal direction (i.e. in the absence of gravity forces) between two adjacent compartments N and N−1 of the same size (TCOM) may be described by

$$FLOW(N)=AVDIF(N)*(WC(N-1)-WC(N))/TCOM \quad (6.1)$$

If the water content is expressed in $cm^3$ water $cm^{-3}$, the thickness in centimeters and the flow in $cm^3$ water $cm^{-2} day^{-1}$, the diffusivity is in $cm^2 day^{-1}$.

This expression for the flow of water seems to be the same as the expressions which were used to describe the flow of molecules in solution or the flow of heat, but there is an important and fundamental difference. For diffusion of heat or solutes, the conductivity and the diffusion coefficient hardly depend if at all on the concentration of the diffusing agent. Thus their values could be calculated from the physical status of the soil in the initial part of the programs. However, the diffusivity for water decreases with decreasing moisture content of the soil, because the frictional forces per unit volume of water increase as the pores that are filled with water become smaller. In Fig. 24, it is shown that according to Hanks & Bowers (1962), the diffusivity of the soil 'Geary silt loam' may decrease more than a 100-fold with a decrease in water content from saturation to 10% volume of water.

Let us consider now a situation where water is absorbed by a soil column. The driving force is hardly dissipated in the wet end of the column because the diffusivity is high and it is not dissipated in the dry zone of the column because there is still no water that is able to move, so that the well-known sharp wetting-front results, which is given in Fig. 25 for Geary silt loam.

The form of this curve has to be simulated by distinguishing a limited

74

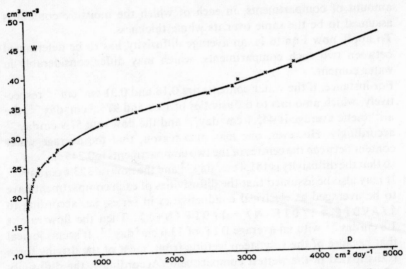

Fig. 24 | Relation between diffusivity (D) and water content (W) for Geary silt loam.

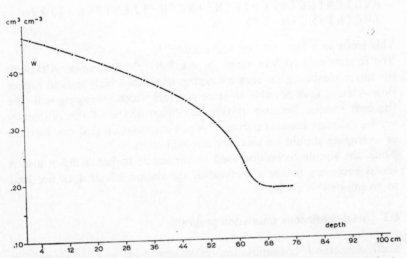

Fig. 25 | Wetting front at 0.6 day after the beginning of an infiltration in Geary silt loam with an initial water content of 0.188 cm³ cm⁻³.

amount of compartments, in each of which the moisture content is assumed to be the same over its whole thickness.

To apply now Eqn (6.1), an average diffusivity has to be determined between two such compartments, which may differ considerably in water content.

For instance, if the water contents are 0.18 and 0.31 $cm^3 cm^{-3}$ respectively, which amounts to diffusivities of 13.8 and 976.3 $cm^2 day^{-1}$, the arithmetic average is 445.1 $cm^2 day^{-1}$ and the flow rate 57.9 $cm day^{-1}$ accordingly. However, one may also reason, that the average water content between the centres of the two compartments is 0.245 $cm^3 cm^{-3}$, so that the diffusivity is 181.4 $cm^2 day^{-1}$ and the flow rate 23.6 $cm day^{-1}$.

It may also be assumed that the diffusivities of each compartment have to be averaged as electrical conductivities in series, i.e. according to $1/AVDIF = 1/DIF(N) + 1/DIF(N+1)$. Then the flow rate is 1.8 $cm day^{-1}$ with an average D I F of 13.6 $cm^2 day^{-1}$. It seems logical that because of the very steep wetting-front, most of the driving force is dissipated in the wettest compartment. Accordingly, the diffusivity of this compartment must be weighted more than that of the drier compartment and this weighting may be done by taking the 'wet average' according to:

$$AVDIF=(WC(N)*DIF(N)+WC(N-1)*DIF(N-1))/ (WC(N)+WC(N-1))$$

This leads to a flow rate of 82.5 $cm day^{-1}$.

The four calculated flow rates show a fortyfold difference. Although the latter reasoning favours averaging methods which lead to higher flow rates, it is impossible to state a priori which averaging will give the best results. Because of the curvilinear shape of the diffusivity versus moisture content curves, it is not even certain that one method of averaging should be used for any soil type.

Thus, the simple technique used so far seems to break down and it seems necessary to use a method of simulation which does not lead to an impossible choice.

## 6.2 Semi-continuous simulation program

Such a method of simulation of water flow was developed by Wagner (1952) for use on an analog computer. It was assumed that the diffusivity decreases exponentially with the moisture content. This method will be presented here in CSMP, which has the great advantage that no assumption about the shape of the diffusivity versus moisture content curve has to be made.

Up to now, any reference to differential equations has been avoided. But in this section, they will be used as otherwise the formulations become cumbersome. In order not to lose the reader who has proceeded this far without a working knowledge of differential calculus, care is taken to explain all mathematical operations.

The conventions used up to now are not very suitable for differential calculus and are therefore changed here by rewriting Eqn (6.1) as

$$(FLOW)_N \simeq \left( D \frac{\Delta W}{\Delta X} \right)_N$$

in which $\Delta X$ is the distance between the centres of two compartments, $\Delta W$ the difference in water content, $D$ the average diffusivity between the compartments $(FLOW)_N$ the flow of water from compartment $N-1$ to $N$. The equal sign is replaced by the about equal sign, to stress that the equation is an approximation, because the gradient in moisture content from one compartment to the other is not linear over finite distances.

The net flow into the Nth compartment may be estimated by substracting the flow out of Nth compartment:

$$F_N \simeq \left( D \cdot \frac{\Delta W}{\Delta X} \right)_N - \left( D \cdot \frac{\Delta W}{\Delta X} \right)_{N+1}$$

It is now assumed that with infinitesimally small compartment sizes, presented by the symbol $dX$, the equation is correct, i.e. that

$$F_N = \left( D \frac{dW}{dX} \right)_N - \left( D \frac{dW}{dX} \right)_{N+1} \tag{6.2}$$

in which $dW$ represents the difference in moisture content over the infinitesimally small distance $dX$. In the infinitesimally small time $dT$ this net flow of water causes an increase in water content of the Nth compartment with thickness $dX$

$$dW = \frac{F_N}{dX} dT \tag{6.3}$$

Substituting Eqn (6.3) in Eqn (6.2) gives

$$\frac{dW}{dT} = \frac{d\left(D\,\dfrac{dW}{dX}\right)}{dX} \tag{6.4}$$

in which $d(D.dW/dX)$ is the differential of the product of diffusivity and moisture gradient at the top and the bottom of the compartment $dX$ and $D$ is the diffusivity at the moisture content of the compartment $dX$.

This differential equation for the flow of water in a porous medium contains two independent variables: the distance $X$ and the time $T$. These occur only in the combination $dT/dX^2$, and for this reason they may be substituted by one variable, which transforms the differential equation into a more suitable form for integration. This procedure is called the Boltzmann transformation.

The new variable equals

$$L = XT^{-\frac{1}{2}} \tag{6.5}$$

Differentiating this variable with respect to $X$ gives

$$\frac{dL}{dX} = \frac{1}{\sqrt{T}} \quad \text{or} \quad dX = \sqrt{T} * dL \tag{6.6}$$

and differentiating to $T$ gives

$$\frac{dL}{dT} = -\tfrac{1}{2}X . T^{-1.5} \quad \text{or} \quad dT = -\frac{2T}{L} * dL \tag{6.7}$$

The Eqns (6.6) and (6.7) for $dX$ and $dT$ are now substituted in the differential Eqn (6.4)

$$\frac{dW}{-\dfrac{2T}{L}\,dL} = \frac{d\left(D.\dfrac{dW}{\sqrt{T \cdot dL}}\right)}{\sqrt{T}.dL}$$

This results after multiplication by $-\dfrac{2T}{L}$ in

78

$$\frac{dW}{dL} = -\frac{2}{L} \frac{d\left(D \cdot \frac{dW}{dL}\right)}{dL}$$

This is a differential equation in the independent variable $L$ only. Remembering that the differential quotient of the product of the functions $U$ and $V$ with respect to an independent variable $L$ is

$$V \cdot \frac{dU}{dL} + U \cdot \frac{dV}{dL},$$

the relation

$$\frac{dW}{dL} = -\frac{2}{L}\left(\frac{dW}{dL} \frac{dD}{dL} + D \cdot \frac{d^2 W}{dL^2}\right)$$

holds, in which $d^2 W/dL^2$ is short hand for the differential quotient of the differential quotient of the water content with respect to the variable $L$. Writing this second order differential explicit gives

$$\frac{d^2 W}{dL^2} = -\frac{1}{D}\left(\frac{dD}{dL} + \frac{L}{2}\right)\frac{dW}{dL} \tag{6.8}$$

This differential equation contains the differential quotient of the diffusivity with respect to $L$, which is eliminated with the chain rule:

$$dD/dL = (dW/dL) * (dD/dW)$$

So that at last

$$\frac{d^2 W}{dL^2} = -\frac{1}{D}\left(\frac{dW}{dL} \cdot \frac{dD}{dW} + \frac{L}{2}\right)\frac{dW}{dL} \tag{6.9}$$

The absorption of water by a uniform horizontal, semi-infinite soil column with a constant initial water content ($IW$) throughout its whole length, is now considered under the supposition that one end of the column is kept at saturation water content ($WS$). The initial value of the water content (at $L = 0$) is then $WS$, but the initial value of $dW/dL$ depends on $IW$ in a way which is determined by the form of the diffusivity function. Hence simulations should be carried out with various initial values of $dW/dL$ and then the water contents obtained with sufficient large values of $L$ should be graphically related to these initial slopes.

The simulation program proceeds as follows:
In order to avoid confusion of symbols it is convenient to rename the internal variables TIME and FINTIM with

    RENAME TIME = L, FINTIM = FINL

Since there are no initial calculations, the INITIAL and DYNAMIC cards may be omitted and because no arrays are involved, the sort option is used by omitting the NOSORT card. This has the advantage that the program no longer has to be written in procedural fashion, so that readability is improved. This advantage is only of importance in large programs of which an example is given by Penning de Vries (1971).

The second order differential quotient of the water content with respect to L, according to Eqn (6.9) is

    D2WL = (-1/D)*(D1WL*DDW+L/2)*D1WL

L is the independent variable, tracked by CSMP. D is the diffusivity which is read from the tabulated function by

```
D = AFGEN(DTBLE,W)
FUNCTION DTBLE = (0.18,13.8),
(0.19,31.1),(0.20,48.4),(0.21,65.7),
(0.22,82.1),(0,23,110.6),(0.24,165.9),
(0.25,197.8),(0.26,285.2),(0.27,407.8),
(0.28,507.2),(0.29,648.0),(0.30,749.9),
(0.31,976.3),(0.32,1123.2),
(0.33,1321.9),(0.34,1555.2),
(0.35,1840.3),(0.36,2160.0),
(0.37,2514.2),(0.38,2808.0),
(0.39,3110.4),(0.40,3386.8),
(0.41,3646.1),(0.42,3888.0),
(0.43,4121.3),(0.44,4164.5),
(0.45,4199.1),(0.46,4200.9).
```

with the water content (W) in $cm^3 cm^{-3}$ and the diffusivity in $cm^2 day^{-1}$.

DDW is the slope of the diffusivity curve with respect to W and again read from a tabulated function by

```
DDW = AFGEN(DDWTB,W)
FUNCTION DDWTB = (0.18,1770),
(0.19,1770),(0.20,1770),(0.21,1730),
(0.22,2245),(0.23,4190),(0.24,4360),
(0.25,5920),(0.26,10500),(0.27,11100),
(0.28,11910),(0.29,14380),(0.30,16460),
(0.31,16480),(0.32,17280),(0.33,21600),
(0.34,25920),(0.35,30240),(0.36,33690),
(0.37,32400),(0.38,29810),(0.39,28940),
(0.40,26780),(0.41,25060),(0.42,23760),
(0.43,13820),(0.44,3890),(0.45,1730),
(0.46,1730).
```

with the water content in $cm^3 cm^{-3}$ and the slope in $cm^2 day^{-1}$.
The value of the first order differential of W is now obtained by integrating D2WL:

```
D1WL = INTGRL(ID1WL,D2WL)
```

and the water content by integrating D1WL:

```
W = INTGRL(WS,D1WL).
```

The initial value of W equals the water content at saturation and is given by

```
PARAMETER WS = 0.46   cm³cm⁻³
```

The initial values of D1WL are in an unknown way related to the initial water content IW of the column, so that the simulation has to be carried out for a range of values, which are successively:

```
PARAMETER ID1WL = (-1.5E-4,-3.E-4,
-4.5E-4,-6.E-4,-7.5E-4,-9.E-4,
-10.5E-3,-1.2E-3)
```

Later it is convenient to use the 'sorptivity' of the soil to compare infiltrated amounts. This sorptivity is calculated with

```
S = INTGRL(0.,W)
SORP = S-L*W
```

For this kind of problem it is wise to use the integration method of Runge-Kutta with variable time-step, which is achieved with

```
METHOD RKS
```

The values of L at which the simulation is finished, and at which output is required are specified with

```
TIMER FINL=150.,OUTDEL=5.
```

and the output is obtained on a plot with

```
PRTPLT W(0.,0.50,SORP)
```

This statement gives a graph of W with a scale of $0.$ to $0.50$ and a table of the sorptivity. The program is finished with

```
END
STOP
```

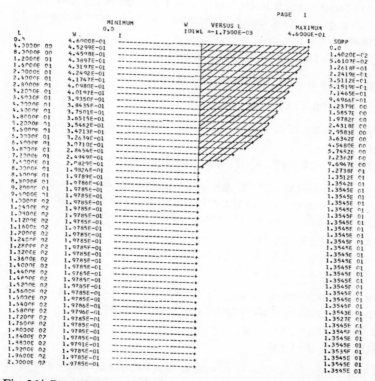

Fig. 26 | Part of the print-plotted output of the semi-continuous program. The shaded area is the sorptivity.

An example of the output is given in Fig. 26. The sorptivity is the shaded area, the shading being entered by the draftsman and not by the computer.

An alternate solution, based on Eqn (6.8) is

```
D2WL=(-1/D)*(DDL+L/2)*D1WL
DDL=DERIV(IDDL,D)
D1WL=INTGRL(ID1WL,D2WL)
W=INTGRL(WS,D1WL)
```

in which the function DERIV takes the derivative of the second argument with respect to the independent variable L (or TIME). The initial values of the derivative function (IDDL) and of the first derivate of W(ID1WL) are then in the initial section related by the chain rule. The advantage of this method is that it is unnecessary to introduce manually the relation between W and the derivate of D with respect to W. But its disadvantage is that the derivative function is less sophisticated than some of the integration procedures.

The curves that show the relation between the water content and L for 5 initial values of the slope are given in Fig. 27. For a constant value of $t$ each curve shows the relation between water content and

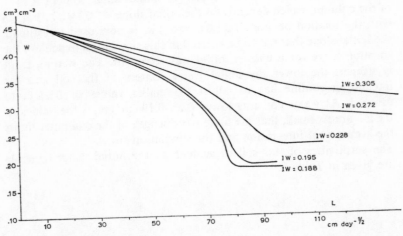

Fig. 27 | Relation between water content (W) and $x/\sqrt{t}(L)$ for different values of the initial water content (IW).

83

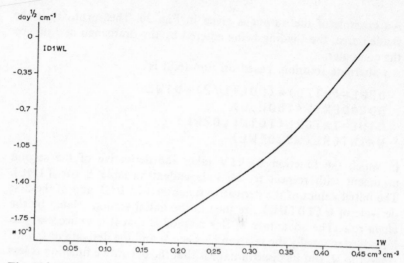

Fig. 28 | Relation between initial slope ( I D 1 W L ) and initial water content ( I W ) for Geary silt loam.

distance from the wet end of a column with the corresponding initial water content. All curves approach an initial water content ( I W ) of the column, which depends on the initial slope ( I D 1 W L ). Fig. 28 with the relation between I D 1 W L and I W, is now used to estimate the initial slope that has to be entered in this simulation to achieve the sorption-curve for a chosen initial water content. The wetting front is steeper, the lower the initial water content of the soil and the integration routine has to adjust to smaller values of DELT, to proceed. At water contents lower than 0.19 cm³ cm⁻³ the values of DELT are so small, that the finite word length of the computer limits the accuracy of integration and the simulation stops.
The sorptivities of this soil dependent on the initial water contents are given in Table 6.

*Table 6*  Sorptivities in cm day$^{-\frac{1}{2}}$ dependent on the initial water content for Geary silt loam.

| initial water content | 0.1888 | 0.1952 | 0.2409 | 0.2561 | 0.2728 | 0.3565 | 0.3791 | 0.4207 |
|---|---|---|---|---|---|---|---|---|
| sorptivity | 14.55 | 14.37 | 12.81 | 12.14 | 11.43 | 7.11 | 5.70 | 2.64 |

## 6.3  Compartmentalized simulation program

The simulation program discussed in the previous section, can only be used for a uniform soil with initially a constant water content throughout and when gravity is not involved. This is not flexible enough to simulate actual situations. Hence, it is still necessary to develop a compartmentalized simulation program, so that the problem of deciding on the proper method of averaging diffusivities and on an acceptable size of the compartments has still to be solved. To find a solution, the results of a compartmentalized simulation model for various methods of averaging are compared with the results of the semi-continuous model of the previous section, assuming that the method of averaging which is best in this situation, is also the best in more complicated cases.

Eqn (6.1) which governs the flow between two compartments does not contain the flow due to gravity forces. When the pressure due to gravity is in cm water, the gradient in vertical direction is in cm cm$^{-1}$ or a dimensionless value. Hence this additional flow may be simply accounted for by adding the average conductivity in cm day$^{-1}$ to the right side of Eqn (6.1), which gives

$$\mathtt{FLOW(N)=AVDIF(N)*(WC(N-1)-WC(N))/}$$
$$\mathtt{TCOM+AVCOND(N)} \qquad (6.10)$$

The value of the diffusivity and conductivity are related through the capacity, or the slope of the suction curve ('pF-curve') of the soil in cm$^3$ water cm$^{-3}$ soil cm$^{-1}$ water pressure, by

$$\mathtt{DIF=COND/CAP}$$

The suction curve and the conductivity curve for Geary silt loam are given in Figs 29 and 30.

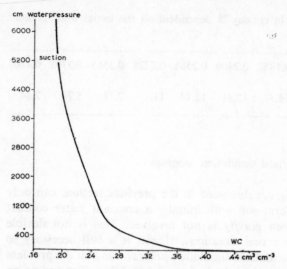

Fig. 29 | Relation between matric suction and water content for Geary silt loam.

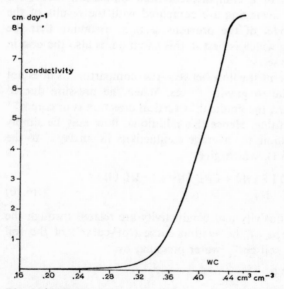

Fig. 30 | Relation between capillary conductivity and water content for Geary silt loam.

The following simulation program contains the essentials to proceed. It is again started with

```
INITIAL
NOSORT
FIXED I,N
PARAMETER N=25
```

The thickness of the compartments is

```
PARAMETER TCOM=4
```

and the initial water contents of the 25 compartments are

```
STORAGE IWC(25)
TABLE IWC(1-25)=25*0.1888
```

so that the initial amount of water in each compartment is calculated with

```
DO 1 I = 1,N
IAMW(I)=IWC(I)*TCOM
1 CONTINUE
```

and the depth with:

```
DEPTH(1)=0.5*TCOM
DO 2 I = 2,N
DEPTH(I) = DEPTH(I-1)+TCOM
2 CONTINUE
```

The direction of gravity is given by:

```
PARAMETER GRAV=0.
```

The value zero, indicating a horizontal, the value $+1$, a vertical column. It is supposed that at time zero the surface is set at a water content WS, which is given also as a parameter.

```
PARAMETER WS=0.46
```

The conductivity in $cm\,day^{-1}$ and the diffusivity in $cm^2\,day^{-1}$ of the soil, dependent on water content in $cm^3$ water $cm^{-3}$ soil, are given as tabulated functions with

```
FUNCTION DIFTB = (0.18,13.8),
(0.19,31.1),(0.20,48.4),(0.21,65.7),
(0.22,82.1),(0.23,110.6),(0.24,165.9),
(0.25,197.8),(0.26,285.2),(0.27,407.8),
(0.28,507.2),(0.29,648.0),(0.30,749.9),
(0.31,976.3),(0.32,1123.2),
(0.33.1321.9),(0.34,1555.2),
(0.35,1840.3),(0.36,2160.0),
(0.37,2514.2),(0.38,2808.0),
(0.39,3110.4),(0.40,3386.8),
(0.41,3646.1),(0.42,3888.0),
(0.43,4121.3),(0.44,4164.5),
(0.45,4199.1),(0.46,4200.9)

FUNCTION CONDTB = (0.18,0.00006),
(0.19,0.00009),(0.20,0.0002),
(0.21,0.00048),(0.22,0.00081),
(0.23,0.0011),(0.24,0.0016),
(0.25,0.0024),(0.26,0.00062),
(0.27,0.0151),(0.28,0.0188),
(0.29,0.0324),(0.30,0.0535),
(0.31,0.08),(0.32,0.1261),
(0.33,0.1814),(0.34,0.2618),
(0.35,0.3681),(0.36,0.5685),
(0.37,0.7344),(0.38,0.864),(0.39,1.27),
(0.40,1.96),(0.41,2.42),(0.42,2.88),
(0.43,3.75),(0.44,4.16),(0.45,4.20),
(0.46,4.24).
```

The diffusivity and conductivity at the surface of the soil are now obtained with

```
DIFS=AFGEN(DIFTB,WS)
CONDS=AFGEN(CONDTB,WS)
```

This is the end of the initial section.
The dynamic section starts again with

```
DYNAMIC
NOSORT
```

At first, the water content of each layer is calculated from the amount of water in each layer with

```
DO 3 I = 1,N
WC(I)=AMW(I)/TCOM
```

which is then used to calculate the conductivity and diffusivity of each layer with

```
COND(I)=AFGEN(CONDTB,WC(I))
DIF(I)=AFGEN(DIFTB,WC(I))
3 CONTINUE
```

The program enables the diffusivity and conductivity between the compartments to be averaged according to various methods. For this a parameter, which specifies the method of averaging is introduced:

```
PARAMETER W=-1.
```

in which −1. indicates that the 'wet-weighted' average is used, 1. that the arithmetic average is taken, 2. that the values for the overlaying compartment are given with double weight and so on.

The weighing factor between the compartments is then calculated with

```
DO 4 I = 2,N
RATIO = WC(I-1)/WC(I)
WF = INSW(W,RATIO,W)
```

For W is negative, the value of RATIO is given to WF and for W larger than zero, the value of W itself. The average values are then obtained with

```
AVCOND=(WF*COND(I-1)+COND(I))/(WF+1.)
AVDIF = (WF*DIF(I-1)+DIF(I))/(WF+1.)
```

and the flow rate from one compartment to the next with

```
FLOW(I)=AVDIF*(WC(I-1)-WC(I))/
TCOM+AVCOND*GRAV
4 CONTINUE
```

The flow rate from the surface to the first compartment is calculated with

89

```
WF = INSW(W,WS/WC(1),W)
AVCOND=(WF*CONDS+COND(1))/(WF+1.)
AVDIF=(WF*DIFS+DIF(1))/(WF+1.)
FLOW(1)=AVDIF*(WS-WC(1))/(0.5*TCOM)+
AVCOND*GRAV
```

The flow from the 25th to the 26th compartment is again set to zero with

```
FLOW(26)=0.
```

which means that the simulation may proceed as long as the change in water content in the 25th compartment is small. Independent of the specified finish time, the simulation may be stopped by

```
CHANGE=ABS((WC(25)-IWC(25))/IWC(25))
```

a function which calculates the absolute value of the relative change in the 25th compartment and the finish condition

```
FINISH CHANGE = 0.10
```

This line states that the simulation is halted as soon as the change in the last compartment is larger than 10%.
The net flow into each compartment is now calculated with

```
DO 5 I = 1,N
NFLW(I)=FLOW(I)-FLOW(I+1)
5 CONTINUE
```

and the integration carried out with

```
AMW1=INTGRL(IAMW1,NFLW1,25)
/EQUIVALENCE (AMW1,AMW(1)),(IAMW1,
IAMW(1)),(NFLW1,NFLW(1))
```

It is useful to integrate at first with the method of Runge Kutta, and to try out later whether less sophisticated methods may be used. The total infiltration is calculated with

```
INFL=INTGRL(0.,FLOW(1))
```

At every output time specified by OUTDEL (compare Section 4.2), the sorptivity may be calculated with

90

```
A=IMPULS(0.,OUTDEL)
IF(A*KEEP.LT.0.5) GO TO 6
SORP=INFL/SQRT(TIME+NOT(TIME))
```

in which the function SQRT takes the square root of TIME+
NOT(TIME). NOT(TIME) is 1 for time is 0 and 0 for time
greater than zero, and thus prevents the order to take the square root
of zero. The value of the variable L, out of the previous program is
for the successive compartments obtained with

```
DO 7 I = 1,N
L(I)=DEPTH(I)/(SQRT(TIME+NOT(TIME)))
7 CONTINUE
6 CONTINUE
```

The output has to be organised by using FORTRAN capabilities, as
in Section 3.
The selection between various methods of averaging is made on the
basis of a graph of the sorptivity against time, presented in Fig. 31.
The horizontal line shows the sorptivity calculated with the semi-
continuous method and the curves with other methods. For a short
time period, the compartments are too large to obtain good results,
but after 0.5 days stationary values are obtained. The arithmetic
average (W=1) gives the best results but the wet average (W=-1)

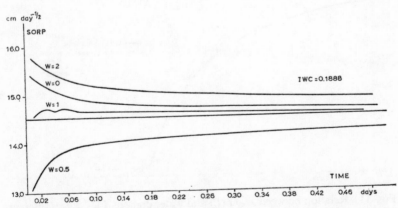

Fig. 31 | The value of the sorptivity (SORP) as a function of time for
different averaging procedures.

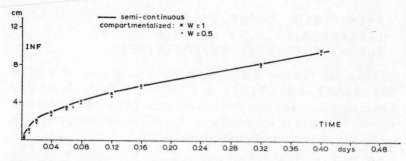

Fig. 32 | Cumulative infiltration curves for different averaging procedures, in comparison with the semi-continuous solution.

is a good second. The vertical scale is very much extended, so that the agreement is somewhere within the fourth digit, which is more than accurate enough for practical purposes.

Infiltration, dependent on time, is shown in Fig. 32. The semi-continuous method is given as a line and two methods of averaging as points. In Fig. 33 the water content in relation to the variable $L$ ($=DEPTH * TIME^{-\frac{1}{2}}$) is given. It is seen in Fig. 33 that some 'tailing' of the graphs is obtained with the 'compartmentalized'

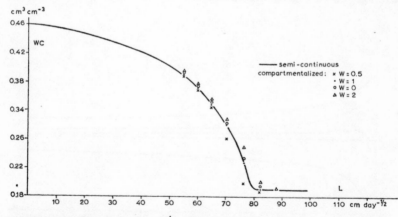

Fig. 33 | Relation between $x/\sqrt{t}$ ($L$) and water content ( WC ) for different averaging procedures, in comparison with that relation from the semi-continuous program.

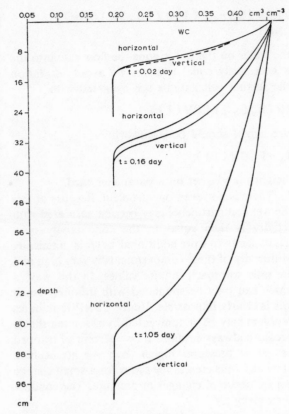

Fig. 34 | Water content (WC) as a function of depth on different times, for horizontal as well as for vertical flow.

simulation program, although the sorptivities are correct. Fig. 34 illustrates the influence of gravity on the infiltration curves. The influence is relatively small so that no appreciable mistake is likely to be made by averaging the conductivities between compartments in the same way as the diffusivities.

The situation is now considered in which a layer of water is brought on the soil at the start of the experiment and gradually diminishes by infiltration. This additional pressure height H is accounted for by calculating the flow rate into the first compartment by

$$FLOW(1)=AVDIF*(WS-WC(1))/(0.5*TCOM)+\\(H+GRAV)*COND$$

However, when all the water on the soil is gone the flow rate into the first compartment is necessarily equal to zero. To avoid oscillation of H around zero, the further calculations are bypassed with

$$FLOW(1)=INSW(H,0.,FLOW(1))$$

Of course the pressure height should be traced with

$$H=INTGRL(IH,-FLOW(1))$$

in which the initial height may be set on a parameter card.
This is all very simple. There is however, one problem. Because of this additional pressure the wet compartments may become saturated with water. Their conductivity is then equal to the conductivity of a saturated soil and their capacity to store additional water is practically zero. Therefore, the diffusivity of these compartments is very high and consequently the flow rates approach infinite values. In this way, a situation develops which can only be simulated with infinitely small time intervals, and this is clearly impossible. Hence CSMP terminates the simulation. The problem may be circumvented by assuming that a soil at atmospheric pressure always contains a few percent of trapped air, which is compressed at pressures higher than one atmosphere according to Boyle's law and thus creates the space for a small change in water content under influence of changes in pressure. The conductivity of the soil is then given by

$$COND=(\frac{CONDA}{WCA})*WC$$

in which the symbols with an A indicate values at atmospheric pressure. The diffusivity at pressures higher than one atmosphere may then be calculated from the conductivity, and the change in volume of air with one centimeter increase of pressure. At an atmospheric pressure of 1000 cm water this change in volume equals $10^{-3}$ times the air content, so that at higher than atmospheric pressures the equation

$$DIF=(\frac{CONDA}{WCA})*WC/(10^{-3}*ACA)$$

holds for the diffusivity.

By including these relations the simulation proceeds, but still the time intervals are very small and lead to long computation times. However, it has been shown, as it can be shown by theoretical reasoning, that the influence of any additional pressure head resulting from a small layer of water on the soil, is negligible for practical purposes. Hence, apart from cases where the interest centres around this problem, it is most sensible to forget about the additional pressure of this layer.

The driving force is not proportional to the difference in water content of two adjacent layers, when their moisture characteristics (i.e. pF-curves) are not the same. In that situation, the Eqns (6.10) and (6.11) should be combined into:

$$\mathrm{FLOW(N) = AVCOND(N)} \frac{\mathrm{P(N-1) - P(N) + TCOM}}{\mathrm{TCOM}}$$

in which the potentials ( P ) at each time-step and for each compartment are calculated from the water contents with the suction curves (pF-curves) of the appropriate soil in each compartment. Of course, the suction and conductivity curves for each soil type in the profile should then be entered as tabulated functions. In the simulation program it is then assumed that the wet average may be used also for the conductivities, although this cannot be proven by comparison with a semi-continuous solution.

The above mentioned approach was applied by van Keulen & van Beek (1971) to calculate the formation of pools during showers, on non-plowed and plowed soil, with and without a hardpan due to plowing.

The relation between the moisture content on one hand and the diffusivity, the conductivity and the suction pressure shows hysteresis: air is trapped during the wetting phase, so that at the same moisture content the water is differently distributed over the pores than during the drying phase. The effect of hysteresis may be included in programs, which simulate alternate wetting and drying cycles. However, it should be stressed that moisture characteristics vary so much from place to place under field conditions, that this degree of sophistication is often not worth the trouble.

## 6.4 Time constant dependent on water content and size of compartments

In the simple case of heat and salt diffusion, it was found (Section 2.3) that the time constant of the system is given by

$$TC = \frac{TCOM^2}{D}$$

in which the diffusivity $D$ was independent of the temperature or the concentration of salt itself, so that, irrespective of the state of the system, the time constant was proportional to the thickness of the (smallest) compartment squared.

For the flow of water, the diffusivity varies with the water content, and moreover, the time constant is not only determined by the diffusion flow of water, but also by the gravity flow. To estimate the time constant, the situation of Fig. 35 will be considered, in which a soil, wet at the top is in contact with a somewhat drier soil at the bottom. The net flow into the bottom compartment is the sum of the net diffusion and net gravitational flow

$$NF = NDF + NGF$$

The diffusion flow out of the bottom compartment is zero, so that $NDF = D * (\Delta W / \Delta X)$ in which $D$ is an average diffusion coefficient between both slabs. The net gravitational flow is

$$NGF = (C1-C2)*1/1,$$

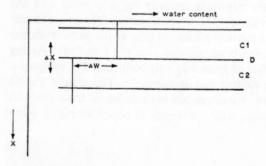

Fig. 35 | Schematic representation of the water content in two adjacent compartments.

i.e. the difference in conductivity, as the gradient is $1\ \mathrm{cm\,cm^{-1}}$.
Since $C2$ is approximately equal to

$$(C1 - (\mathrm{d}C/\mathrm{d}W) * \Delta W)$$

in which $\mathrm{d}C/\mathrm{d}W$ is the slope of the conductivity curve at the average water content, the net gravitational flow equals

$$\mathrm{NGF} = C1 - (C1 - (\mathrm{d}C/\mathrm{d}W) * \Delta W) = (\mathrm{d}C/\mathrm{d}W) * \Delta W$$

Now this system certainly starts oscillating, if the water content of the compartment increases in one time interval with $\Delta W$. Hence the time interval should be smaller (for instance 1/5) of the time constant $\Delta T$, calculated from:

$$\Delta W * \Delta X = \mathrm{NF} * \Delta T$$

The resulting expression is:

$$\Delta T = \Delta X^2/(D + (\mathrm{d}C/\mathrm{d}W) * \Delta X) \tag{6.11}$$

From Eqn (6.11) can be seen, that for $\Delta X \ll D/(\mathrm{d}C/\mathrm{d}W)$ the time constant increases quadratic with increasing $\Delta X$, but for $\Delta X \gg D/(\mathrm{d}C/\mathrm{d}W)$ the time constant increases only linearly with $\Delta X$.

For Geary silt loam, with a water content of $.45\ \mathrm{cm^3\,cm^{-3}}$, $D$ and $\mathrm{d}C/\mathrm{d}W$ equal $4200\ \mathrm{cm^2\,day^{-1}}$ and $4\ \mathrm{cm\,day^{-1}}$ so that $D/(\mathrm{d}C/\mathrm{d}W)$ is about 1000 cm. Hence with compartments of 4 cm, the time constant is about equal to

$$\Delta X^2/D = 16/4200 = 4*10^{-3}$$

For a dry soil, with a moisture content of $.20\ \mathrm{cm^3\,cm^{-3}}$, $D$ and $\mathrm{d}C/\mathrm{d}W$ equal $48.4\ \mathrm{cm^2\,day^{-1}}$ and $2*10^{-2}\ \mathrm{cm\,day^{-1}}$, respectively, so that $\Delta X$, at which $D$ and $(\mathrm{d}C/\mathrm{d}W) * \Delta X$ are equal, assumes a value of 2500 cm.

The time constant for 4 cm compartments is then $16/48.4 \approx 0.35$ day. At higher than atmospheric pressure the conductivity and the diffusivity are, as explained in Section 6.3, equal to

$$\mathrm{D = CONDA/WCA*WC/(10^{-3}*ACA)}$$

and

$$\mathrm{d}C/\mathrm{d}W = \mathrm{CONDA/WCA}$$

so that the time constant equals

$$\Delta T = \Delta X^2 / (WC/(10^{-3} * ACA) + \Delta X) * WCA/CONDA =$$
$$= \Delta X^2 / (0.46/(10^{-3} * 0.05) + \Delta X) * 0.46/4.24,$$

which equals for compartments of 4 cm:

$$16/(0.46/(5 * 10^{-5}) + 4) * 0.46/4.24 \approx 2 * 10^{-4} \text{ day}.$$

for Geary silt loam with 5% included air at atmospheric pressure. The penalty for extending the present program in this way, is therefore very high in terms of computer costs. The difficulty may be overcome by introducing soil sections in the simulation program, with stationary flow of water, but this is beyond the scope of this book.

# References

Brunt, D., 1932. Notes on radiation in the atmosphere I. Q. J. Roy. Met. Soc. 58: 389–420.

Carslaw, H. S. and C. J. Jaeger, 1962. Conduction of heat in solids. Clarendon Press, Oxford.

Frère, M. H. and C. T. de Wit, 1971. Computer modeling of nutrient movement in soils. Symp. 6th Intern. Coll. on Plant Analysis and Fertilizer problems, Tel Aviv, 1969.

Frissel, M. J., P. Poelstra and P. Reiniger, 1970. Chromatographic transport through soils. Plant and Soil, 33: 161–176.

Glueckauf, E., 1955. The theoretical plate concept in column separations. Trans. Faraday Soc. 51: 34–44.

Hanks, R. J. and S. A. Bowers, 1962. Numerical solution of the moisture flow equation for infiltration into layered soils. Soil Sci. Soc. Amer. Proc. 26: 530–534.

Heald, W. R., M. N. Frère and C. T. de Wit, 1964. Ion adsorption on charged surfaces. Soil Sci. Soc. Amer. Proc. 28: 622–627.

IBM, 1969. System/360 Continuous System Modelling Program (360-A-CX-16X). User's Manual, H20-0367-2. Techn. Publ. Dept., White Plains, USA.

Keulen, H. van and C. G. E. M. van Beek, 1971. Water movement in layered soils. A simulation model. Neth. J. Agric. Sci. 19: 138–153.

Lambert, J. R. and F. W. T. Penning de Vries, 1971. Dynamics of water in the soil-plant-atmosphere system: A model named TROIKA. Proc. Symp. of the Intern Soc. of Soil Science on Soil Water Physics and Technology, Rehovoth.

Milne, E. W., 1960. Numerical solution of differential equations. McGraw-Hill, New York.

Penman, H. L., 1948. Natural evaporation from open water, bare soil and grass. Proc. Roy. Soc., London, 193: 120–145.

Penning de Vries, F. W. T., 1971. A model for simulating transpiration of leaves with special attention to stomatal functioning. J. appl. Ecol. 9: 57–77.

Vervelde, G. J., 1955. A physico-chemical analysis of salt accumulation by plant roots. Plant and Soil, 6: 226–244.

Vries, D. A. de and C. T. de Wit, 1954. Die thermischen Eigenschaften der Moorböden und die Beeinflussung der Nachtfrostgefahr dieser Böden durch eine Sanddecke. Meteor. Rundschau, 7: 41–45.

Wagner, C., 1952. Journal of Metal Trans 4: 91. Cited through: Crank, J., 1956. The mathematics of diffusion Oxford Univ. Press, London.

Wierenga, P. J. and C. T. de Wit, 1970. Simulation of Heat Transfer in Soils. Soil Sci. Soc. Amer. Proc. 34: 845–847.

Wijk, W. R. van, ed. 1963. Physics of Plant Environment. North-Holland Publishing Co., Amsterdam.